Hot Topics in Financial and Legal Matters for General Practice

Mike Gilbert, Ben Willis and Oliver Pool

Hot Topics in Financial and Legal Matters for General Practice

Mike Gilbert, Ben Willis and Oliver Pool

Royal College of
General Practitioners

The Royal College of General Practitioners was founded in 1952 with this object:

'To encourage, foster and maintain the highest possible standards in general practice and for that purpose to take or join with others in taking steps consistent with the charitable nature of that object which may assist towards the same.'

Among its responsibilities under its Royal Charter the College is entitled to:

'Diffuse information on all matters affecting general practice and issue such publications as may assist the object of the College.'

British Library Cataloguing-in-Publication Data
A catalogue record for this book is available from the British Library

© Royal College of General Practitioners, 2015
© The Authors, 2015
Published by the Royal College of General Practitioners, 2015
30 Euston Square, London NW1 2FB

Designed and typeset by Prepress Projects Ltd
Printed by Lightning Source UK Ltd
Indexed by Susan Leech

ISBN 978-0-85084-388-0

CONTENTS

About the authors

Mike Gilbert is a chartered accountant who has specialised in medical practice finance and taxation for over 30 years. Being the son of a dedicated GP, Mike was brought up in an environment of medical practitioners and spent the first ten years of his life living above the surgery premises. He is accepted as a leading authority on the subject and is in considerable demand as a lecturer to doctors and practice managers alike, and for contributions to the medical press.

Mike also writes and comments extensively for medical journals. He is the Editor-in-Chief of the Association of Independent Specialist Medical Accountants (AISMA) publication *Managing Money for General Practitioners* and is currently responsible for the AISMA annual survey into the accounts for GPs and the subsequent production of national benchmarking profiles.

Mike was a founder member of AISMA and served as its Chairman from 1997 to 2002. Mike set up a specialist medical division for an accounting firm in Newcastle upon Tyne in 1991 and, by the time he left in 2013, they served 150 medical practices together with many consultants, locums and other healthcare professionals. Mike currently acts as a consultant for BW Medical Accountants of Newcastle upon Tyne and Honey Barrett of Bexhill-on-Sea, both of whom are accounting firms specialising in the medical sector, and assists them in publishing material and conducting workshops.

Ben Willis is a commercial property lawyer with over 20 years' experience of working with both mainstream commercial clients and those operating in the healthcare sector. He is head of the healthcare team at Veale Wasbrough Vizards LLP and has particular expertise in the ownership, development and funding of healthcare property. GP surgery development is an acknowledged specialism and Ben has been involved in over 95 such developments.

Ben takes time to understand the healthcare sector and to establish a strong rapport with clients. This brings a wider perspective to the commercial issues faced by clients and consistently proves to be important in giving the best advice to suit the circumstances. He leads a team of specialist lawyers and has established links with banks and other professionals to complete a strong collaborative approach.

Ben is a member of the Primary Care Premises Forum and the National Association of Specialist Solicitors Advising Doctors (NASSAD), a specialist healthcare lawyers' group. He organises regular healthcare conferences for GP clients, including annual 'Practice Management' conferences for GPs and practice managers in Bristol and Cardiff. They have developed exceptional contacts with banks and other specialist professionals who operate in the healthcare sector and can bring more experience to a situation than just their own legal advice.

Oliver Pool is a partnership lawyer with Veale Wasbrough Vizards LLP who has specialised in advising primary care clients for ten years and has drawn up partnership agreements for over 200 practices. Oliver is the only solicitor sitting on the Institute of Chartered Accountants Special Interest Group committee. He regularly lectures on current legal matters relevant to the GP and practice manager sector.

Ian Crompton is an expert in healthcare banking with many years' experience in the field.

Nick Martindale is an experienced commercial litigator with Veale Wasbrough Vizards LLP. Nick has developed expertise in partnership dispute resolution, particularly for GP practices. With a family background in health care, Nick has an innate understanding of the sector and what makes medics 'tick'.

Scott McKenzie has worked in the healthcare sector for over 18 years. With an extensive commercial background in business, project and account management, Scott's expertise and track record in health care was established following a number of years specialising in the pharmaceuticals sector. Scott is now widely recognised as a specialist provider of support to the NHS on all aspects of service transformation, commissioning and service provision. With his colleagues at BW Medical Accountants, Scott is currently supporting the set-up and ongoing development of GP federations nationally.

Kevin Walker is an independent financial adviser and Director at BW Medical Accountants. He has worked in the financial management industry for over 30 years and has extensive wealth management experience alongside exceptional knowledge and understanding of NHS pensions policy and final-salary pension schemes. His specialist team has developed a bespoke financial model to provide accurate NHS pension forecasts for GPs. Kevin lectures nationally for LMCs, CCGs and has also been a guest speaker for national medical conferences, providing specialist advice and support on NHS pension changes.

Anthony Young is a corporate partner at Veale Wasbrough Vizards LLP and advises entrepreneurs, investors and businesses to realise their ambitions to grow, identify and exploit opportunities and get deals done. He is passionate about networking and making introductions for his clients and contacts. He advises on business and asset sales, joint-venture arrangements, investments and restructuring businesses. He has developed particular expertise in advising GP Federations and provider companies as well as entrepreneurs and private enterprises in the healthcare sector.

PREFACE

Although medical practice itself is a specialist occupation, it has all the trimmings of a 'specialist' business. Practice finance and law is a complex business and it is becoming increasingly difficult to run a successful practice in the present climate. With the pressures facing GPs and practice managers at an all time high it is becoming more and more essential to work 'on' as well as 'in' the practice. To do this practices have to reorganise in order to create time to undertake these hugely important tasks.

To assist GPs and practice managers, we have put together a compendium of hot topics surrounding accounting, banking and legal issues that currently affect most, if not all, practices. The topics are not exhaustive but have been carefully selected to deal with current-day problems. We have attempted to keep the topics wholly up to date but readers should bear in mind that medical practice finance is subject to constant change at relatively short notice, and we are mindful of the fact that the topics will need updating on a regular basis. The rate of change to medical practice finance and law in the past few years has been enormous, and you must therefore seek the most up-to-date advice when making any decisions based on the information included in the topics of this book.

We hope that the topics are easy to read, and throughout there are worked examples and tables that can be lifted and applied to the reader's own circumstances. If this book does not help GPs and practice managers in their own practices then we have failed to achieve our purpose.

We are grateful to all of the contributors and organisations who have helped us to put the topics together, and without their assistance this book would not have been possible. We hope you enjoy the topics and of course we would be more than happy to receive your feedback. The over-riding point that underlies this publication is the recognition of the fact that the most successful practice in terms of earnings, quality of life and, indeed, patient care, find and take the time to work 'on' as well as 'in' the business.

Mike Gilbert
Ben Willis
Oliver Pool

ACKNOWLEDGEMENTS

Mike Gilbert is a consultant for the following three accounting firms who are all members of AISMA: BW Medical Accountants of Newcastle upon Tyne, Honey Barrett of Bexhill, and Moore & Smalley of Blackpool.

He acknowledges with thanks not only their permission for using material specifically written for them but also their valuable contribution to the technical content. He is particularly grateful to Kevin Walker and Scott McKenzie of BW Medical Accountants for their input into the topics of pensions and federations.

Ben Willis would like to acknowledge the strong contributions to this publication made by members of the healthcare team at Veale Wasbrough Vizards LLP, particularly Oliver Pool, who has provided a lot of the technical content relating to partnerships, and to Anthony Young and Nick Martindale for their contributions on business structures and federations and dispute resolution respectively.

The wider healthcare team at Veale Wasbrough Vizards has over 25 years' experience in the primary care sector. Acting for over 400 GP practices, the team enjoys exceptional contacts with other specialist professionals and banks in the sector and can bring more experience to a situation than just legal advice. Clients say that it is the dedication to understanding what is happening in the sector that sets the team apart. The firms operates from three offices, in Bristol, London and Birmingham, and the mature sector experience is complemented by the expertise and national reach that a full-service commercial law firm can bring to bear.

THE GP CONTRACT AND OTHER CHANGES – A ROCKY ROAD AHEAD!

Mike Gilbert

On 15 November 2013 the BMA's General Practitioners Committee (GPC) and NHS Employers (on behalf of NHS England) announced changes to General Medical Services (GMS) contractual arrangements applicable from April 2014.

Having already experienced contract changes for 2013/14 resulting in a fall of earnings for most GPs, these further announcements will again have a significant impact on practice finances, and GPs need to be alert to the effect of the changes on their take home pay. We set out below what the key changes might mean for a typical practice.

Seniority

Seniority payments are being removed over a six-year period commencing from April 2014.

Those who were not already in receipt of seniority payments by 31 March 2014 are not entitled to receive future seniority payments.

For practitioners currently in receipt of a seniority payment it is expected that payments will continue to be made in line with progression outlined in the Statement of Financial Entitlements (SFE) until 31 March 2020.

However, there is also an expectation that the savings made from retiring GPs, and no new entrants to the scheme, will be at least 15% a year. If that is not the case then it is likely that the amount of seniority per band in the SFE will reduce to ensure that a 15% reduction year-on-year is achieved. This latter point is subject to further agreement between the negotiators and will not be evaluated until the 31 March 2015 data are available, and probably not before September 2016.

Funding released from the seniority pot will be added into global sum payments. The details of this have not been confirmed but, in general, where global sum funding increases, so too proportionately does the amount deducted for out-of-hours.

WHAT MIGHT THE IMPACT BE?

- The incentive to stay longer in general practice or to keep superannuable earnings above the threshold by which seniority is paid in full may be diminished. This could well be an additional factor in the move for longer-serving GPs to reduce their workload commitments or take early retirement.

- This reduces experience and capacity across primary care.
- The redistribution of seniority payments to Personal Medical Services (PMS)/Alternative Provider Medical Services (APMS) practitioners should be redistributed fairly into those contracts on the same basis as the GMS global sum.
- The reinvested funds should be approximately 15 pence per weighted patient a year.

Quality and Outcomes Framework

The major impact of the agreed changes has been in respect of the Quality and Outcomes Framework (QOF), currently worth a maximum of 900 points.

One-hundred-and-eighty-five points of clinical indicators, 33 points of public health indicators, 33 points of patient experience indicators and 100 quality and productivity indicators will be retired. Ten points will be added to the clinical domain for hypertension.

Therefore 238 points worth of the released funding (£37,000 per average practice) will be added into the weighted capitation global sum payment but will not be subject to a 6% deduction for out-of-hours opt-out and will be available to all practices including those with a correction factor. One-hundred-and-three points (worth £16,000 per average practice) is transferred into enhanced services.

The total of available points are 559 for 2014–15. The threshold increases that were previously announced to take effect from April 2014 have been deferred for a further year. Some of the timeframes for reviews have also been increased.

WHAT MIGHT THE IMPACT BE?

- The burden of bureaucracy, unnecessary patient testing and recall, and box-ticking is removed or reduced. But clinicians will continue to use their professional judgement to carry out necessary treatments and so appropriate workload will not reduce but will be funded via the core contract.
- Most of the imposed 2013–14 changes have been reversed.
- QOF payments to practices for 2014–15 will be at least 45% less than received in 2012–13, reducing the average from £21 per weighted patient to about £11.75.
- However, for the money taken out of the QOF and reinvested in the global sum there will be an improvement to overall cashflow. This is because more income will be received within the monthly global sum payment rather than only 70% via the monthly QOF aspiration payments, and then waiting until May/June for a final 30% achievement payment.
- Low QOF performers with high-weighted capitation lists should do well

from the reallocated funding compared with high QOF achievers with low-weighted lists.

- The likely increase to the global sum funding for the QOF reinvestment will be in the order of £5 per weighted patient.

Enhanced services

A new unplanned-admissions enhanced service (ES) commenced on 1 April 2014 for one year. This will be funded by reinvesting 100 QOF points together with £42m from the 2013–14 risk-profiling ES.

A total of £160m is therefore available.

This will involve proactive case management of at-risk patients covering 2% of the over-18 patient population. A personalised care plan will be created that identifies a named, accountable GP.

The dementia ES is to be extended for another year, 50% funding on engagement and 50% on activity evidence.

Learning disabilities, alcohol and extended-hours ESs are all extended for another year. The patient participation ES is retained but funding is reduced to £20m, with the other £40m to be reinvested into core funding.

The remote care monitoring ES and patient online ES ceased on 31 March 2014 and the total £36m funding is to be reinvested into core funding. The risk-profiling ES also ceased at 31 March 2014 and the funding is reinvested into the new unplanned-admissions ES.

WHAT MIGHT THE IMPACT BE?

- There will be no new money. However, for those who were not high earners from or involved in some of the previous ESs then the reinvestment in core funding should be of benefit. Again, this is particularly for those with high-weighted lists.
- There might also be an improvement in cashflow for reinvested money paid monthly rather than paid in arrears on achievement for ESs.
- Money reallocated from the QOF into ESs will be about £2.20 per weighted patient. Money reallocated out of the patient participation ES into the global sum will be about 70 pence per weighted patient, and from the remote care and patient online ESs will be about a further 65 pence.

GP pay and expenses

The Doctors' and Dentists' Review Body (DDRB) will make future recommendations for uplift in the usual way, for consideration by the government.

WHAT MIGHT THE IMPACT BE?

- The DDRB should take into account the continuing inflationary pressures on running costs within general practice and the workload pressures on GPs and their staff to ensure a suitable pay award is recommended.

Minimum Practice Income Guarantee

From April 2014 the correction factor payments used to meet the Minimum Practice Income Guarantee (MPIG) are being phased out over seven years. Funding will be recycled into the global sum. There is further discussion currently underway about possible transitional relief for special circumstances.

WHAT MIGHT THE IMPACT BE?

- All practices in receipt of a correction factor payment will be affected and those with an above average weighted list should benefit. But there will be losers.
- For a typical practice about 60 pence per weighted patient from the correction factor will be reinvested into the global sum.

Publication of earnings

Practices will have to publish GP NHS net earnings relating to the core contract only in 2015–16 using data for 2014–15. A working group is being established on what and how to publish the information.

The calculation will be on a like-for-like basis with other healthcare professionals.

WHAT MIGHT THE IMPACT BE?

- Practices may need to collate their accounting information in a different way or pay their accountants to produce an additional analysis alongside the year-end accounts required for tax purposes.
- It will be vital to ensure clear guidelines are drawn up about how to disclose income streams and the expenditure relating to them. Consideration will need to be given to looking at this on a per patient basis (weighted or raw?).
- There will also be discrepancies to consider where practices might choose to employ salaried GPs compared with practices who share workload among more partners.
- The main difficulty will be in how to make the comparisons fair alongside other healthcare professionals. That will entail thinking about full-time equivalents, numbers of sessions and what is a full-time working commitment.
- All GPs who are members of the NHS Pension Scheme currently have to complete a certificate of their superannuable earnings annually. By definition this quantifies their NHS earnings from the core contract and other sources. It seems to me to be the most suitable template for tailoring into a practice-wide model to calculate the figures that will be required.

PMS contracts

Appropriate changes should be reflected equitably in PMS contracts at a local level.

WHAT MIGHT THE IMPACT BE?

- PMS practices will continue to undergo funding reviews and it may well be time to find out what reverting back to GMS will mean in terms of overall contract funding. If PMS practices have a high-weighted list size their funding gap with GMS may not be as large as they think.

Other changes

A named, accountable GP for all patients will take lead responsibility for the coordination of all appropriate services required under the contract.

Practices who have opted out of out-of-hours will have to monitor the quality of service provided by the out-of-hours provider. Practices will be contracted to take the Friends and Family Test from December 2014.

Since October 2014 practices have been able to register patients from outside their traditional boundary without obligation to provide home visits. NHS England will have the responsibility for in-hours urgent medical care at or near home for such patients.

Care Quality Commission (CQC) inspection outcomes will have to be displayed in waiting rooms and on websites. The weighting given to deprivation will be strengthened in the Carr-Hill formula from April 2015. The existing deprivation factors were updated from April 2014. Practices managing highly deprived populations should see the benefits in due course.

There are also various requirements regarding IT changes for patients and information being applied in 2014–15.

The other UK countries

NORTHERN IRELAND

Contract changes for 2014–15 in Northern Ireland are likely to be similar to England particularly with respect to the QOF (245 points will move into core funding). However, the quality and productivity (QP) targets will be retained.

Discussion is also taking place around federations, commissioning and more equitable funding. There could be increased funding for out-of-hours.

The MPIG has not been phased out but will be part of ongoing discussions to increase funding streams.

SCOTLAND

In Scotland there will be no phasing out of MPIG and there have been minimum changes to the 2014–15 contract.

WALES

The Welsh should have seen a contract deal shortly before we went to press and were expected to follow some of the QOF changes introduced in England; however, they are retaining QP targets.

MPIG is not being phased out in Wales at this stage.

Practices may be paid to work in clusters.

Planning ahead

When the full details are published via the SFE, and in particular how the reinvestment into the global sum will be dealt with, all practices should be in a position to evaluate the likely changes to their income streams.

A profit projection and superannuable earnings projection for 2014–15 can then be produced so that cashflow and drawings expectations can be set from April 2014 at realistic levels.

There does not appear to have been anything negotiated around premises funding so practices will need to think separately about making the most of their premises within existing funding envelopes. However, in his autumn statement of December 2014 the Chancellor announced that there would be £1 billion made available for GP premises, and practices should not be shy in coming forward to bid for funding.

As we go to print contract changes for 2015/2016 have emerged, which can broadly be summarised as follows:

- a named, accountable GP for all patients who will take lead responsibility for the coordination of all appropriate services required under the contract and will ensure they are delivered to each of their patients where required
- no reduction in the size of the QOF although point value to be adjusted to reflect population growth and relative changes in practice size
- access to medical records online
- online appointment booking to be expanded
- GP net earnings to be published
- practices to be entitled to reimbursement of actual cost of GP locum cover either internal or external for maternity, paternity and adoption leave of £1,113.74 for the first two weeks and £1,734.18 thereafter, or the actual costs if lower
- the avoiding unplanned admissions ES extended for a further year
- patient participation ES and alcohol reduction ES to cease on 31 March 2015, with associated funding reinvested in the global sum
- extended hours ES, dementia ES and learning disabilities ES extended for a further year
- Carr-Hill formula to be reviewed to address deprivation
- retrospective mechanism for achieving annual deduction of 15% in seniority now agreed
- correction factor funding moving into the global sum will be reinvested with no out-of-hours deduction applying
- all of the above changes will be reflected in PMS and APMS contracts.

Taxation of earnings for new and old GPs

Mike Gilbert

Given that there is no joint and several liability for a partnership to pay the income tax liabilities of the individual partners, it follows that practice earnings are taxed on the individual. However, some practices still save for tax within the partnership to help individual partners make the necessary savings. Those GPs with flexible mortgages may prefer to use such savings to offset their mortgages. GPs are reminded that they are taxed on what they earn and not on what they draw.

Each partner in a practice needs to complete a self-assessment tax return annually and submit it to HMRC. However, in order to complete this return, the partnership tax return needs to be dealt with first. Both returns are issued in April each year and must be filed online by the following 31 January.

Partnership tax return

This is derived from the accounts of the practice. The profit in the accounts should be adjusted for the following:

- items that are not tax deductible or taxable
- items that are taxed separately – such as taxed interest
- partners' expense claims (if not included in the accounts)
- partners' capital allowances claims (typically cars and computers)
- practice capital allowances claims.

This adjusted profit is then allocated between the partners in their profit-sharing ratios, taking account of items that are prior shared or prior charged to individual partners. The details disclosed for each individual partner are then transferred to their personal tax returns. Where a partnership tax return is submitted late there is an automatic penalty of £100 on each of the partners, which can be quite expensive in a large partnership. Great care needs to be taken not to include income twice where it is retained personally but treated as part of the partnership accounts. Equally it is easy to omit income that was thought to be part of the practice accounts, but was not. Best practice dictates that all income should be included in the practice accounts and anything personal is prior shared to the relevant partner.

The following is a fictitious example of a partnership tax calculation for a three-partner practice for the year ended 31 March 2014:

Profit per accounts				300,000
Add back items that are not tax deductible:				
Depreciation			2,000	
Employer's superannuation (if deducted In accounts)			25,000	
Life assurance			3,000	
				30,000
				330,000
Deduct items that are taxed separately:				
Bank interest			200	
				200
				329,800
Practice capital allowances				3,000
				326,800
Partners' expenses:				
Partner 1			1,200	
Partner 2			500	
Partner 3			1,500	
				3,200
				323,600
Partners' capital allowances:				
Partner 1			500	
Partner 2			750	
Partner 3			200	
				1,450
Taxable profits				£322,150
Allocate the profits:				
Profit-sharing ratios	100	100	75	275
	Partner 1	Partner 2	Partner 3	Total
Prior shares per accounts	12,000	8,000	3,000	23,000
Balance	108,782	108,782	81,586	299,150
Totals	£120,782	£116,782	£84,586	£322,150

Self-assessment tax return

This return takes the figures from the above partnership tax return and includes them on the partnership pages. It will also be necessary to disclose on this return any other income that is not already included on the partner-ship tax return. When the return is completed the tax can be computed at the same time. It should be noted that all individuals are permitted to make some deductions from their total income before it is taxed, including:

- personal allowance
- superannuation contributions paid
- old-style retirement annuity premiums
- loan interest paid on a loan to buy a share of a partnership, or property used by a partnership.

Certain deductions attract tax relief at only higher rates (where the basic rate relief is obtained by paying net of tax in the first place), e.g. gift aid payments to UK charities or personal pension contributions. After these deductions, tax is charged according to rates prevailing in the fiscal year and in addition Class 4 National Insurance (NI) contributions must be paid at the same time. Using the previous example, the personal tax calculations for Partner 1 may look like the following for 2013/14:

Share of partnership profit				120,782
Share of partnership interest				73
Personal interest				500
Total income				£121,355
Deduct:				
	Superannuation contributions		25,000	
	Interest on loan to buy into practice		1,500	
	Personal allowance		9,440	
				35,940
				£85,415
Tax on:				
	First 32,010 at	20%	6,402	
	Balance 53,405 at	40%	21,362	
				27,764
Class 4 NI contributions: on partnership profit less practice interest paid				
	First 7,955 at	0%	–	
	Next 33,910 at	9%	3,052	
	Balance 77,417 at	2%	1,548	
				4,600
Total tax and NI contributions payable for the year				£32,364

NB: the above ignores any charge arising from a breach of the annual allowance for pension purposes.

When is the tax paid?

For a continuing practice, the balance of tax is paid in the January following the end of the tax year (after payments already made on account), and a payment on account for the following year is made at the same time. Then, in July each year, there is a further payment on account. Again using the above example the tax payment profile would be as follows:

Total tax and NI contributions for 2013/14	32,364
Payment dates	
31 January 2014 – 1st payment on account	10,000
(based on 2012/13 tax) say	
31 July 2014 – 2nd payment on account	10,000
	20,000
31 January 2015 – balancing payment	12,364
1st payment on account 2014/15 (half of 2013/14 tax)	16,182
Total due 31 January 2015	£28,546
31 July 2015 – 2nd payment on account	£16,182

NON-31 MARCH YEAR ENDS

Accounts that are made up to 31 March or 5 April are treated as being coterminous with the tax year. If the accounts are made up to any other date in the year, it is the accounts' date ending within the tax year that is used. For example, accounts made up to 30 June 2014 form the basis of the 2014/15 assessable profits. This can cause complications when a GP joins or leaves a practice, and a system of 'overlap relief' ensures that during the career of a GP all profits are taxed, and taxed only once.

Using the profit shares from the above example, let us assume that the results relate to the year ended 30 June 2014 and not 31 March 2014. The share of profits were:

Partner 1	£120,782
Partner 2	£116,782
Partner 3	£84,586

Given that 30 June 2014 falls in the tax year 2014/15, the tax payment dates become:

First instalment	31 January 2015
Second instalment	31 July 2015
Balance	31 January 2016

Consequently tax payments have been deferred by one year from those disclosed in the previous example, although an 'overlap' situation must exist that we will consider below when referring to starters and leavers.

New GP partners

For a new GP partner, the tax situation is completely different as his or her earnings are taxed on an actual basis in the early months of becoming a partner. In the above example let us assume that Partner 3 joined the practice on 1 October 2013. In these circumstances he or she is assessed to tax on the following earnings:

2013/14 Actual earnings 1 October 2013 to 5 April 2014, being $^6/_9 \times £84,586 =$		£56,391
2014/15 Accounts to 30 June do not include 12 months' profit so:		
9 months to 30 June 2014 =	£84,586	
3 months of accounts to 30 June 2015, say	£25,000	£109,586
but thereafter:		
2015/16 Accounts for the year ended 30 June 2015		
Note that there are two overlapping periods where earnings are effectively taxed twice as follows:		
1 October 2013 to 5 April 2014		£56,391
1 July 2014 to 30 September 2014		£25,000
		£81,391

This figure is carried forward as 'overlap relief', which will be claimed on retirement or on leaving the practice because eventually all profits are only taxed once. It is interesting to note that the same overlap scenario applies also to the payment of superannuation contributions.

NEW GP PARTNERS – TAX PAYMENT DATES

Following on from above let us assume that the tax payments are as follows:

2013/14 Assessable profits £56,391 – tax and NI contributions	£12,000
2014/15 Assessable profits £109,586 – tax and NI contributions	£31,000

Assuming that Partner 3 was previously employed and taxed under PAYE, the tax payments become as follows (overleaf):

31 January 2014	No payment on account required as no tax unpaid for 2012–13	
31 July 2014	As above	
31 January 2015	Tax for 2013/14 due	12,000
	plus payment on account for 2014/15	6,000
		£18,000
31 July 2015	Payment on account for 2014/15	£6,000
31 January 2016	Balance of 2014/15	19,000
	plus payment on account for 2015/16	15,500
		£34,500
31 July 2016	Payment on account for 2015/16	15,500

31 January 2015 and 31 January 2016 may come as a nasty shock!

By way of comfort, it is worth noting that Partner 3 pays no tax until 31 January 2015, which means that he or she has had a 16-month tax holiday. The system works in such a way that new GP partners have to be aware of the tax 'lumps' in early years.

Retiring, leaving and the overlap tax time bomb

The situation is best explained by keeping rigidly to the above examples. Assume that Partner 3 leaves the practice on 30 June 2018 and that his or her assessable profits for that year were, say, £120,000.

Partner 3's tax for 2017–18 was based on the year to 30 June 2017.

Thus for 2018/19 he or she is taxed on:

The full year to 30 June 2018	12 months	£120,000
Less overlap relief	9 months	81,391
Being fiscal year	3 months	£38,609

In addition, for 2018–19 he or she will be taxed on new earnings from 1 July 2018 to 5 April 2019.

Thus, after Partner 3 leaves the practice he or she will still pay tax on practice earnings as follows:

31 July 2018	2nd payment on account for 2017/18
31 January 2019	Balance of 2017/18
	1st payment on account of 2018/19
31 July 2019	2nd payment on account 2018/19
31 January 2020	Balance of 2018/19

If the payments on account are not sufficient, he or she could still be paying tax until 31 January 2020 having left the partnership on 30 June 2018.

The tax time bomb now becomes clear. Given that Partner 3 was only at the practice from 6 April 2018 to 30 June 2018 in the fiscal year 2018/19, he or she might expect to be taxed on approximately one quarter of his or her annual earnings, say, one quarter of £120,000 = £30,000, but he or she is actu-ally assessed on £38,609 (above). Furthermore Partner 3 will have used up his or her allowances and basic rate tax band so that his or her earnings from 1 July 2018 to 5 April 2019 will all be taxed at a higher rate. The bigger the gap between starting earnings and leaving earnings the worse the problem becomes. So beware the overlap tax time bomb!

THE OVERLAP TAX TIME BOMB

Mike Gilbert

All GPs who are self-employed partners in a practice that has an accounting year end date of anything other than 31 March have to be aware of the potential tax liability that awaits them when they retire or leave the practice for any other reason. This liability arises because of the 'overlap' of accounting periods on which the GP is assessed for tax. This can best be explained by considering the example of a Dr A.

Dr A joined a four-partnered practice on 1 September 2010 on a fixed share of income of £72,000 p.a. (after the practice has paid his employer's superannuation contributions) for the first ten months, after which he became a parity partner. The accounting year end of the practice is 30 June. Thus far his earnings have been:

1 September 2010 to 30 June 2011 (10 months, $^{10}/_{12}$ of £72,000) =	£60,000
1 July 2011 to 30 June 2012 (1 year)	£96,000

The important issue is how these earnings fall to be taxed in the relevant fiscal years. The situation is as follows:

FISCAL YEAR	
2010/11, based on period 1 September 2010 to 5 April 2011,	
Being £60,000 × $^{7}/_{10}$	42,000
2011/12, based on first 12 months in practice	
Being 1 September 2010 to 30 June 2011	60,000
Plus 1 July 2011 to 31 August 2011 (£96,000 × $^{2}/_{12}$)	16,000
2012/13, based on year to 30 June 2012	96,000
TOTAL EARNINGS ASSESSED TO TAX OVER THREE FISCAL YEARS	£214,000

It can be seen that there are two overlapping periods in the above calculations. These enable us to calculate the 'overlap' relief to carry forward to retirement or on leaving the practice, as follows:

1 September 2010 to 5 April 2011	42,000
1 July 2011 to 31 August 2011	16,000
	£58,000

This overlap relief therefore represents nine months of earnings that have effectively been assessed to tax twice in the above calculations for which relief is given at a later date. So what is the problem? The problem is that Dr A has deferred tax to be paid back at a later date. The potential liability is calculated as follows:

Nine months of current earnings, say £96,000 × $^9/_{12}$	72,000
Less: nine months of overlap relief carried forward	58,000
	£14,000
Potential future tax liability at 40%	£5,600

Thus in less than two years Dr A has created a tax time bomb for the future of £5,600, and it is essential he is aware of this situation to enable him to plan his future career path. Indeed, the situation could get significantly worse because, although his income will increase over the years if for no other reason than inflation, the overlap relief is not index linked in any way. Thus current earnings in several years' time may well be greater than the overlap relief of £58,000.

GPs might be forgiven for claiming that to avoid this future problem it is better to pay tax on an actual basis and therefore have an accounting year end date of 31 March or 5 April. But is this strictly correct? What actually happened is that Dr A would have paid an extra £5,600 tax in 2010/11, 2011/12 and 2012/13 in order to save it at a later date. In other words, by having the 30 June year end, Dr A has deferred £5,600 in tax payments to pay at some future unspecified date. By way of proof we can consider the earnings that would have been assessed to tax had the practice had a 31 March year end.

2010/11, based on period 1 September 2010 to 31 March 2011, Being $^7/_{10}$ × £60,000	42,000
2011/12, based on year to 31 March 2012, being $^5/_{12}$ × £72,000 Plus $^7/_{12}$ of £96,000, i.e. £30,000 plus £56,000	86,000
2012/13, based on year to 31 March 2013, say	100,000
TOTAL EARNINGS ASSESSED TO TAX OVER THREE FISCAL YEARS	£228,000

With a June year end we already know (from above) that the total earnings assessed to tax over the same three fiscal years was £214,000
Excess of March year end over June year end £14,000
Tax at 40% £5,600

Thus it is clear that from a taxation point of view GPs should not be too eager to change the accounting date. The simple question is 'Do you want to pay tax now or defer it until later?' If the latter option is taken, GPs should know the extent of the 'overlap' tax time bomb and plan for it accordingly.

Sadly the 'overlap' problem does not end there. The same situation applies to the calculation of superannuation payments so that, again, arbitrarily high contributions may be experienced on retirement or on leaving a practice, because earnings at that time could be significantly higher than when the overlap relief was set up. Advice should be taken as to the best date for retirement in order to minimise the problem so far as is possible.

Topic 4

THE 'QUALITY' PRACTICE

Mike Gilbert

During our role in facilitating away days, some GPs express the desire to run a quality medical practice. But how can we define a quality practice and who is competent and able to judge? The simple fact of life is that patients take clinical and technical performance for granted and are totally incompetent to judge a 'great' doctor. There is no product as such, and rather than providing cures for ailments doctors actually deliver solutions to problems.

It follows that we have to kill the myth – quality does not equal clinical excellence. Doctors can only differentiate from the rest by the manner in which they deliver because reality is what the patients perceive clearly. Thus quality is all about raising perceptions and lowering expectations, or, put another way, quality equals perceptions minus expectations.

So how do practices and individual GPs manage perceptions and expectations? They do so by recognising and dealing with the five quality service dimensions in order of importance, which are:

1. Reliability
- Keep patients informed during the process.
- Never over-promise (lower expectations).
- Deliver early (raise perceptions).
- If appropriate, follow up discussions with letter or email.
- Hire capable staff, train them and reward them.
- Deal with complaints properly and promptly.

2. Assurance
- Demonstrate concern.
- Respect confidentiality at all times (patient records and reception).
- Communicate well (if possible turn bad news into good news).

3. Tangibles
(This is the only visible dimension; the others are subjective.)

- Provide up-to-date leaflets on topical concerns.
- Exhibit only relevant posters.
- Remember that any 'souvenir' provides a clue to the quality of service.
- Keep up-to-date facilities and equipment.
- Be mindful of the state of the reception area.
- Dress for success.
- In all aspects a high-quality appearance improves perception.

4. Responsiveness
- Timeliness of service (set standards on replies to calls, emails and letters).
- Approachability (enough telephone lines and availability of appointments).
- Do not keep patients waiting for long.

5. Empathy
- Commitment and understanding – TLC.
- Know the name of spouse, children, dog and know the patient's hobbies.
- Be considerate of patients' time.
- Friendliness of practice staff.

Reliability is the most important because if GPs deliver more than expectations their patients become their best advocates.

Given the above, it follows that all staff must be involved in delivering a quality practice. Indeed, reception has more moments of truth than anyone else in the practice. Perceptions are based on contact, and practice staff have more contact than the GPs. They can make or break the patient relationship, and have the best chance of directing patients to the most appropriate services and of detecting the needs of patients. Quality is about people, and it improves communications, team spirit, objectives and practice structure so that the whole team is moving in the same direction. In this respect, training is crucial as the GPs cannot succeed without the staff team. GPs should regularly ask staff what they think, how the practice can be improved, and what the practice should do.

No one can deny that it is not easy to provide a quality service. There are indeed several quality service problems to be solved along the way, such as:

- production and consumption is simultaneous – everybody in the practice interacts with patients
- operational support – patient records, filing, library updates and reception
- communications shortfall – over-promising is the issue, and good intentions are no good at all as they are perceived as failure. Practices sometimes

fail to keep in touch properly with patients or misunderstand patient communications

- viewing patients as statistics by not knowing their names
- short-term view of the practice by making old equipment last
- service proliferation and complexity whereby some GPs may not be wholly committed to the practice.

The key to success is for GPs and practice staff to recognise that they must manage their moments of truth by controlling expectations during the service provision and perceptions after the service provision. The following are some ideas designed to help during the process:

- do not over-promise
- deliver early
- beware extremists or expectations, i.e. the grumblers or flatterers
- remain positive rather than defensive
- emphasise you can influence events, not control them
- communicate – stay in touch
- follow up critical discussions with letter or email
- turn bad news into good news
- put new flowers in reception weekly
- produce quarterly practice newsletters but about patients as well as you
- demonstrate you care at all times and value the relationship
- establish quality standards for the practice
- hire capable practice staff
- train practice staff to meet quality standards
- monitor quality of performance with patient surveys
- reward outstanding performance
- deal with complaints properly and handle them well:
  - deal with them willingly
  - listen
  - show understanding and concern
  - mutually agree on a solution
  - follow through and learn from mistakes.

Overall, remember that the satisfied patient is where perceived quality exceeds expectations, and the dissatisfied patient is where expectations exceed perceived quality.

It cannot be coincidence that once a quality practice is established that the practice tends to feature amongst the higher earners in the profession. The logical conclusion is that a quality practice is able to create that most important commodity of all – time! By creating time the opportunity to maximise practice income is significantly enhanced so that the best possible result can be achieved – money and lifestyle all in one!

FIVE STEPS TO TAKE BEFORE CUTTING YOUR DRAWINGS

Mike Gilbert

The potential loss of income from the global lump sum, Quality and Outcomes Framework (QOF) and enhanced services is worrying GP partners, with commentators predicting that many will need to take the drastic measure of cutting their drawings. How do you determine whether this is a necessary option? Start by considering the following questions:

1   Is the bank balance deteriorating to the extent that overdraft facilities may be required when hitherto this was not necessary?
2   Is the monthly salary bill increasing at a significant rate?
3   Are there any signs of increasing delays in the payment for enhanced services and other income streams?
4   Are you considering if there is any scope to delay the payment of practice overheads invoices?
5   Is there a large capital expense coming up?
6   Are you expecting potential claw backs of practice income such as seniority?
7   Will funds be needed to pay out a retiring partner?

Also remember that an individual partner's drawings can be increased, e.g. after a 24-hour retirement when employers' and employees' superannuation contributions are no longer payable.

Now take into account the following tips:

1. Study the partners' current accounts set out in the latest set of practice accounts

The fictional accounts of Upside Medical Practice for the year ended 31 March 2013 serve as a good example (overleaf):

Partners' current accounts at 31 March 2013

	Dr A	Dr B	Dr C	Dr D	Dr E	TOTAL
	£	£	£	£	£	£
At 1 April 2012	7,032	6,934	7,245	7,271	7,183	35,665
Profit for the year	118,933	127,839	126,106	124,929	124,274	622,081
	125,965	134,773	133,351	132,200	131,457	657,746
Monthly drawings	89,254	100,228	99,349	97,806	104,283	490,920
Equalisation drawings	1,032	934	1,245	1,271	1,183	5,665
Seniority drawn	9,979	7,866	7,637	7,637	5,129	38,248
Class 2 NI contributions	130	130	130	130	130	650
Loan repayments	5,000	5,000	5,000	5,000	0	20,000
Employee superannuation	12,638	13,299	12,616	12,606	12,917	64,076
	118,033	127,457	125,977	124,450	123,642	619,559
At 31 March 2013	7,932	7,316	7,374	7,750	7,815	38,187

The partners are aware that each year they need to allow between £30,000 and £40,000 to finance the day-to-day working capital requirements of the practice (represented by the total figure on the top line of £35,665 at 1 April 2012). They also know that 2013/14 will see a further rise in employee superannuation contributions, although if profits fall the impact may not be too great.

2. Analyse what will happen to profits in 2013/14

Study every line of the most recent profit and loss account, and forecast what is likely to happen in the year to 31 March 2014, starting with income. Be conservative when estimating QOF points to be achieved and enhanced services to be performed. Think laterally, using these tips to help the process:

- have we the skills to provide services that may be more lucrative than QOF points or enhanced services?
- can we get involved in 'providing' either by ourselves or in collaboration with other practices?
- are we performing work that should be delegated to other members of the staff team?
- can we create time to supplement our income with outside work?
- what different opportunities might there be to generate new income streams in our locality and with our skills and resources?

When undertaking the above you must consider the recent contract and other changes, the main issues being as follows:

a   The phasing out of the correction factor (the Minimum Practice Income Guarantee – MPIG) over seven years b   QOF changes such as the increase to the upper thresholds for indicators, the reform of the Contractor Population Index, the reduction of total points to 900 and the shifting of points to new clinical areas

c   The GMS uplift of 1.32%

d   The new enhanced services in the areas of rotavirus, shingles, seasonal flu, MMR catch-up, risk profiling, dementia cash funding, online patient access and remote cash monitoring

e   Other changes such as responsibility of locum employer pension contributions, rebate of £2,000 employers' NI contributions, and increase in GP employee superannuation contributions.

3. Review all practice expenses

Starting with staff costs, remember that in the year ended 30 September 2012 there was a 10% increase in staff numbers in UK general practice. Consider the staff mix. Look at training needs and work together as a team.

Letting people go prematurely means that you could find that you do not have the capacity to deal with the expected workload or new profitable income streams.

The most obvious costs to consider are stationery (and in particular computer paper), telephone invoices, insurances, locum costs, subscriptions and repairs/maintenance.

Consider service and expertise, and be especially careful with professional fees, e.g. for legal and accountancy services. Price decisions alone can easily lead to a false economy.

When reviewing practice overheads remember that you might only get one opportunity to make cuts. At the same time you could consider joining a buying consortium for drugs and other medical supplies. Many practices are now considering outsourcing various management costs but care should be taken as such services no longer become unique to your practice and you may be better off continuing to go it alone. If the practice can become a 'provider' of certain medical services then the formation of federations with other practices may prove to be beneficial in terms of the sharing of costs.

4. Reconstruct the partners' current accounts

Having followed the advice above, now reconstruct the partners' current accounts for the year ended 31 March 2014 to determine what the impact will be on monthly drawings.

The fictional partners at Upside Medical Practice calculate that in the coming year practice profits will fall by approximately 5% to £590,000. They took some equalisation drawings in April 2013 and know that employee superannuation contributions have already gone up. They also know they need to allow

£35,000 to finance the working capital of the practice. The balancing figure has to be taken from the monthly drawings. Working with the practice accountant, they reconstruct the partners' current accounts as follows:

Partners' current accounts at 31 March 2014

	Dr A	Dr B	Dr C	Dr D	Dr E	TOTAL
	£	£	£	£	£	£
At 1 April 2013	7,932	7,316	7,374	7,750	7,815	38,187
Profit for the year	112,517	121,422	119,690	118,513	117,858	590,000
	120,449	128,738	127,064	126,263	125,673	628,187
Equalisation drawings	932	316	374	750	815	3,187
Seniority drawn	9,900	7,800	7,600	7,600	5,100	38,000
Class 2 NI contributions	130	130	130	130	130	650
Loan repayments	5,000	5,000	5,000	5,000	0	20,000
Employee superannuation	13,691	14,449	13,666	13,654	14,011	69,471
Monthly drawings	83,796	94,043	93,294	92,129	98,617	461,879
	113,449	121,738	120,064	119,263	118,673	593,187
At 31 March 2014	7,000	7,000	7,000	7,000	7,000	35,000

Thus, the monthly drawings of each partner will be cut as follows:

	2013	2014	CHANGE
	£	£	£
Dr A	7,438	6,983	-455
Dr B	8,352	7,837	-515
Dr C	8,279	7,774	-505
Dr D	8,150	7,677	-473
Dr E	8,690	8,218	-472

A further downside may relate to the payment of income tax. Remember that the income tax payments for the year ended 31 March 2013 occur in January 2013, July 2013 and January 2014. Initially these will be based on profits from the previous year to 31 March 2012 so that the reduction in profit leading to reduced drawings will not have an immediate taxation effect. It follows that a reduction in profits in the year to 31 March 2014 will not have a tax payment effect until 31 January 2015. If the practice saves for income tax on behalf of the partners, the above needs to be taken into account when calculating drawings levels.

5. Backdate cuts to drawings appropriately

When should the cut to drawings take place? The answer is now and the cuts should be backdated to 1 April 2013 by using simple arithmetic.

Don't forget to review the position regularly. GP partners will want to know if the cut is too conservative or indeed too drastic. The answer lies in the monitoring of the bank account (or control of cash flow). If the bank balance remains fairly consistent or static the cut is about right. If the bank balance shows signs of a downward trend then the cuts are not sufficient. If the bank balance shows an upward trend then the cuts may be too drastic and the GPs can have a one-off special draw later in the year.

Looking forward, there are other issues that could affect drawings down the years. In particular, the following issues may be relevant:

a   If a partner retirement is looming in the short term, the other partners need to consider whether the replacement will be a partner, salaried GP or other health professional. A new partner may preserve the status quo whereby the outgoing partner is paid out effectively by the incoming partner. Additional profit may be achieved by recruiting a salaried GP, but the cash received from the excess profit may have to be used to pay out the retiring partner's share, rather than immediately becoming available to take as drawings by other partners. Consider using a bank loan instead

b   If the practice has a mortgage connected to the surgery premises, review when interest rates might change and what might be the effect on the monthly repayment. When is the loan facility due for review? Will further capital have to be repaid in the short term? How will this be financed other than by reducing the sums of money available for drawings?

c   Although overall list sizes in the UK are not significantly changing, it is worth reviewing the practice demography to see what effect it might have on future global sums, QOF and enhanced services

d   Above all, consider where you can save time to create the opportunity for earning non-contractual income.

PARTNER ROLES

Mike Gilbert

It is entirely up to individual practices as to how they structure both the business management and medical workforce within their walls. The ideal practice structure is geared to maximise earnings either through efficiency or the creation of time. It is clear that the highest earning practices are well organised and well run along business lines. In this context partner roles are crucial to the process as all partners should share the feeling of responsibility for income generation.

For the purpose of this Topic we will not consider clinical roles, which are most often obviously assigned. In other words we are concerned with working 'on' the practice as opposed to 'in' the practice. It is important that roles are allocated to the best person for each job, so although some of the tasks can be delegated to the practice manager they will not be abdicated. Partners should be given protected time for management so that the job will be done more effectively, the benefit of which almost invariably outweighs the cost to the practice.

Each partner with specific roles should report on his or her role to the other partners at a formal monthly partner meeting. This is where the other partners can support or block a proposal and generally have their say on a particular issue. It follows that each role will have a place on the partnership meeting agenda. In this way, the democratic process will be protected because it is at the partners' meeting where all significant strategic decisions are taken. A partner with a specific role cannot make unilateral decisions. He or she can do the research and make proposals but it is the partners who have the final say. It is therefore extremely important to ensure that the partnership agreement is clear as to how many partners constitute a quorum for meeting purposes, what decisions require a simple majority or unanimity, and who if anyone has a casting vote.

Bearing in mind there might be some overlap in the roles, we now need to consider what are the most appropriate management roles in the modern-day medical practice and how they are undertaken.

Managing partner/chief executive

This person is the recognised leader of the practice who chairs partners' meetings, speaks at 'all hands' meetings and oversees all of the other roles within the practice. He or she is always the second port of call for advice, grievances, ideas and suggestions.

Outside interests/private work

Often undertaken by the managing partner, this person 'flies the flag' for the practice in the outside world, whether it be at the Clinical Commissioning Group (CCG), Local Medical Committee (LMC), British Medical Association (BMA), local government or Royal College of General Practitioners (RCGP), and researches opportunities for non-contractual work. Other partners may well be involved but reporting directly to the managing partner.

Systems

This partner has a crucial role in constantly reviewing the systems and protocols undertaken by the practice, and researching better ways of doing things. This of course will include the use of information technology. To undertake this task, the systems partner may well form a sub-committee to include the practice manager and other key members of the staff team. In larger practices more than one partner may be involved.

Finance

The finance partner is likely to set up a sub-committee to include the practice manager and other key members of the staff team with a view to overseeing the practice finances and reporting back to the other partners. He or she will take a particular interest in the monthly payroll and General Medical Services (GMS) or Personal Medical Services (PMS) schedules, and monitor the bank balance. He or she will be responsible for ensuring that all matters are up-to-date and that the accountants have all the information they require.

Premises

Again, the formation of a sub-committee may be desirable. The role involves not only exploring alternative sites but also dealing with the existing premises to include the lease (if any), decoration, repair, car parking, layout of the consulting and other rooms, and in particular the appearance of the reception area. Valuations, extensions, rent reviews and all other property issues come under this remit.

Human resources/training

This is one of the most difficult roles in any practice and the person allocated this role will need to attend employment seminars and courses. A sub-committee will be necessary to include the practice manager and other senior members of staff representing all of the functions of the practice. This partner will be the first port of call for all grievances and disciplinary issues. Job specifications and training will be central to this role, and skills mix must always be a major consideration. Much of the day-to-day matters will be delegated to the practice manager, but this partner must be involved because the staff team have more 'moments of truth' with patients than the partners.

Nursing and other clinical staff

This role does not include the human resource administration, which is dealt with by the previous partner (see above). The role is more involved with the work undertaken by the nursing team and other clinical staff, and the identification of specific skills, services and mode of operation. The partner is likely to attend regular meetings with the clinical staff to discuss their work. It is quite astonishing how often the clinical team have clinical skills that the partners were hitherto unaware of, so that in many instances partner time can be freed up or new services can be provided. This role is often undertaken by a GP trainer.

Federating/provisioning/services

The role of this partner is to communicate with other local practices with a view to bidding for services that the practice has the skills to perform. More often than not this will involve attending federation and other meetings to represent the practice. A lead role should be sought to enable the practice to get into a good position to bid for and provide services. Joint working will be the key, but this partner needs to ensure that the practice has the necessary skills to participate. He or she must also negotiate with local government, foundation trusts, social services and other community bodies in the pursuit of service provision.

***

The size and nature of the practice will determine the precise roles and the number of roles each partner must undertake. As most of the roles require sub-committees, all of the staff team will be involved somewhere or other, and as intimated earlier more than one partner could sit on a particular sub-committee.

The final point revolves around the length of time a partner should be in a particular role and when a role should be changed. In an ideal world a role should last, say, three years and then rotated but there is no fixed rule – a particular partner may have a special acumen for a subject. If a partner is not suited to a particular role, then a change can be made by the partners at any partners' meeting. Age and experience are not the criteria to follow.

Once the partners' roles are set, the practice should be able to draw a clear organisational chart whereby everybody in the practice will know their duties and obligations, and to whom they are reporting. The systems sub-committee should also put together a procedures or protocol manual, which should be brief and to the point. In this way, the practice will establish a 'brand', hopefully the envy of others, which will assist them to face all of the challenges to medical practice along the way, and enable them to leave a great legacy for all future partners.

PARTNERSHIP DISPUTES – THE ACCOUNTANT'S PERSPECTIVE

Mike Gilbert

It is a sad fact of life that people for whatever reason 'fall out'. Occasionally, but fortunately not too often, partners in a medical practice get involved in a dispute, which may arise from a misunderstanding of financial accounts, a disagreement over finances and profit shares generally, personality issues, clinical performance or differences surrounding practice strategy.

As one might expect the solution to the problem is to have a well-drawn-up partnership agreement, which should:

- reduce the risk of contentious and expensive disputes
- protect the financial interest of each partner
- satisfy the interest of Clinical Commissioning Groups (CCGs) and NHS England
- enable GPs to write their own rules
- deal effectively with the appointment and retirement of partners.

In particular, there should always be a clause which states that the partnership as between the continuing partners should not come to an end on a partner leaving the practice for whatever reason.

In the absence of a partnership agreement there is a 'partnership at will', which means that relations between partners are governed by the Partnership Act 1890. This is an unstable business relationship that could have the following consequences:

- a notice may be served by any one partner on the others without their prior knowledge or consent, which takes immediate effect, and no reason need be given to justify it
- the notice may result in the forced sale of all partnership assets (including surgery premises) and the redundancy of all staff – this creates the potential to incur considerable financial loss
- both parties incur considerable professional fees because lawyers and accountants will be engaged to sort out the mess

- following dissolution, some of the partners may wish to set up in practice again, but there is no guarantee that they will be able to obtain a new GMS or PMS contract
- there is no restrictive covenant.

GPs are therefore advised to ensure that they have a valid partnership agreement. In particular, a new partnership agreement or deed of variation needs to be signed on admitting a new partner, which may of course provide for a period of mutual assessment. Much has already been written in connection with the contents of a partnership agreement, but from a financial point of view the following items are critical:

- the basis of valuation of surgery premises
- what constitutes partnership income and what constitutes private income
- what expenses are paid by the partnership and what expenses are to be met privately
- prior shares and charges
- how superannuation contributions are to be dealt with.

The following case study, taken from a true situation but 'doctored' to protect anonymity, deals with a dispute arising from a misunderstanding of financial accounts. It relates to a GMS dispensing practice consisting of five partners, where Dr A retired on 30 June 2012. Relations between the partners were not particularly good and there was a change of practice accountants on 1 July 2012, so that the new accountants would prepare the practice accounts for the year ended 30 June 2013.

On 30 June 2012, the balance sheet of the practice disclosed the following (approximately):

	£	£
Surgery premises (1) at valuation	375,000	
Surgery premises (2) at valuation	75,000	
	450,000	
Less: property loan	(350,000)	
		100,000
Fixtures, fittings and equipment		
at book value		20,000
Current assets		
Stock of drugs	45,000	
Debtors and prepayments	75,000	
Cash at bank and in hand	10,000	
	130,000	

Current liabilities		
Creditors and accrued charges	60,000	70,000
		190,000
Represented by:		
Property capital accounts (£20,000 each)		100,000
Partners' current accounts:		
Dr A	20,000	
Dr B	19,000	
Dr C	17,500	
Dr D	18,000	
Dr E	15,500	
		90,000
		190,000

It was left to the previous accountants to provide advice on the pay-out to the retiring Dr A. The first stage of the transaction was undertaken correctly – the practice agreed to pay Dr A £20,000 for his share in the equity of the surgeries and release him from all liabilities connected to the property loans. The practice also agreed to pay him his partner's current account, being £20,000 at 30 June 2012.

The situation then went 'belly up'. For some inexplicable reason, the previous accountants advised that Dr A was also entitled to his share of the value of drugs stock and fixtures, fittings and equipment at 30 June 2012, which they calculated at £13,000 (probably £45,000 stock plus £20,000 fixtures etc., at his share of 20% = £13,000). The practice consequently paid out £53,000 to Dr A.

In September 2013 the new accountants prepared the practice accounts for the year ended 30 June 2013. These accounts showed that Dr A had overdrawn £13,000 that was due back to the practice. This is because the £13,000 paid to Dr A, for stock and fixtures and fittings etc., was in fact a 'double count' in that these items are already included in his partners' current account as demonstrated by the balance sheet at 30 June 2012, above, which of course *balances*. The partners' current accounts are represented by the fixtures and fittings, drug stock, debtors and bank accounts, less liabilities – it is therefore clearly a double count if Dr A receives more than his partners' current account for these items.

The practice rightly requested the return of £13,000 from Dr A. Dr A was surprised to receive this request and could not understand why he had been overpaid. He sought advice from the previous accountants and his solicitors, and ultimately refused to repay the £13,000. Through his solicitor and accountant, Dr A contended that the practice claim of £13,000 was spurious and that he had correctly been paid out in accordance with the instructions of the previous accountants. On the advice of the new accountants and the practice solicitor, the continuing partners issued a formal demand on Dr A for £13,000.

The demand surprisingly was defended with vigour, and legal proceedings duly ensued. To this day it remains a mystery why the defendants could not understand what a relatively simple accounting concept it is. Nevertheless, substantial costs were incurred by both sides, including the cost of employing barristers! In an attempt to settle the matter, the practice said they were prepared to accept £10,000 in full and final settlement but for reasons best known to himself Dr A appeared to want his day in court.

To cut a long story short, Dr A rightly lost heavily in court, being obliged not only to repay £13,000 to the practice but also the legal costs of both sides, which amounted to a staggering further £40,000. The moral of the story again is to ensure that proper specialist professional advice is sought to deal with the financial arrangements relating to incoming and outgoing partners, and to remember that legal action based on perceived principles is always going to be an extremely costly experience. It is also worth considering whether such matters are an insurable risk in consultation with specialist medical insurers.

PARTNERSHIP DISPUTES – THE LAWYER'S PERSPECTIVE

Nick Martindale and Oliver Pool

For all involved, partnership disputes are always unpleasant, and almost always expensive. Partnerships are always better off protecting themselves against a dispute arising in the first place, by having a proper partnership deed. That said, sometimes even the best document cannot prevent individuals falling out. Notoriously, when partners fall out, the disputes can be very bitter, which is partly why they can get so expensive. 'Partnership is a relationship closer than marriage', as the saying goes, and the disputes can sometimes have a similar character.

Expulsion

Expelling a partner is not always an easy task. Most partnership deeds will include an expulsion clause of some sort, but usually the bar is set very high. In order to be expelled the partner's behaviour has to be quite clearly unacceptable – most expulsion clauses will provide that partners can only be expelled if they are struck off, guilty of clear financial misconduct, or guilty of some 'flagrantly immoral' act.

If such conduct arises then there is usually little problem in proving the grounds for expulsion, issuing the notice, and excluding the partner. However, few disputes are quite so 'open and shut'. It is far more common that partners simply become unable to work together because of a clash of personalities, but no one has gone quite as far as doing anything actively wrong so as to enable them to be expelled. In such situations, the 'green socks clause' is important.

The green socks clause

The partners should always consider whether to include such a clause in their partnership deed – not all practices have one in their agreement. A green socks clause provides that, if all the other partners agree, a 'troublesome' partner can be given six months' notice to leave the partnership. Importantly, there is no need to prove (or even to cite) 'grounds' for expulsion to use one of these clauses – it may simply be that the other partners could not bear working with someone who wears green socks.

Green socks clauses can often function as an effective deterrent to bad behaviour. If partners feel that they have a post as a partner 'come what may' then they have less incentive to act appropriately towards their partners, accept changes with an open mind, and to communicate properly. Partners with such security can become 'difficult'. In our experience, partners who know that they can be asked to leave on six months' notice, if they cease to cooperate with their partners properly, are much less likely to get themselves in that position in the first place. As a firm we have never seen a green socks clause used improperly – but we have seen many practices wish they had one when a dispute has arisen!

Basis for disputes

Whether a partner is expelled on valid grounds, under a green socks clause or simply uses the retirement provisions to leave, there is no guarantee that it will be a smooth exit.

The most bitter fallings-out between partners will likely involve money. Partners may occasionally want to litigate over a point of principle but this is rarely advisable and, given the high legal costs involved, will be a luxury few can afford.

Although partners may only view a dispute as a fight over money (or principle), lawyers will need to consider what legal 'causes of action' each party might have. If there is a partnership deed in place then the dispute will most likely be framed as a breach of the agreement. If there is no partnership deed then it is likely to arise out of the provisions of the Partnership Act 1890 or any actions brought under the common law that have been developed over time. These might include:

- a claim for an account (where money payable between the partners needs to be ascertained and paid)
- breach of various common-law partnership duties (such as the duty of good faith, duty to give information and keep accounts or duty not to compete with the partnership)
- other claims such as negligence, fraud or for a contribution between partners.

Once the legal basis for the dispute has been determined then the potential claimant will need to establish the loss that has arisen as a result. For relatively simple claims this may well be easy to calculate. For more complicated claims, it may be necessary to involve an accountant or other expert early in the process. If the matter proceeds through the courts then a judge is likely to require the assistance of an expert witness at trial. It can be helpful to engage expert witnesses from the off, rather than receive nasty surprises along the way.

Resolving a dispute

Although most people will think that a dispute needs to involve court proceedings, there are various other ways to try to resolve any arguments. In fact, the courts actively encourage the parties in using Alternative Dispute Resolution (ADR for short).

ADR covers a variety of processes but the common theme is that they all require the agreement and commitment of the parties to the process. The options include:

- expert determination – where an independent expert in the subject matter of the dispute is appointed by the parties to resolve the matter. The parties agree to be bound by the expert's decision. This process is likely to be most productive where the dispute is limited in scope
- mediation – is a confidential process that enables both parties to explain and discuss what their needs and concerns are to each other in the presence of an independent third party – the mediator – so that they reach an agreement between themselves
- arbitration – is similar to the court process with an arbitrator, or panel of arbitrators, determining the dispute between the parties. The process is generally more flexible than court proceedings and will, more often than not, be cheaper. However, the flexibility can also allow the process to drag on and the cost of the arbitrator(s), when compared with court fees, can limit the overall cost savings.

Most GP partnership agreements contain clauses that oblige the parties to resolve any disputes through arbitration rather than court proceedings. If the parties have already agreed an arbitration clause in the partnership deed then a court will usually refuse to hear the dispute because it does not have jurisdiction.

The benefit of using ADR is the overall reduced costs and the flexibility of the procedure. Court proceedings, by comparison, will involve a more rigid process and be governed by the Civil Procedure Rules. Court proceedings are likely to last the longer and could take between 12–24 months, depending on the complexities of the dispute and caseload of the relevant court.

Although parties are usually keen to have their 'day in court', the reality is very different. After going through the various stages of case management, disclosure, witness statements and expert reports the parties will already feel quite jaded by the process. However, the pressures only increase as the trial gets closer and the prospect of being cross-examined by a barrister becomes more daunting. It is this kind of pressure that means only a small percentage of issued claims actually go all the way to trial and, if they don't settle at the outset, they will usually settle in the final run-up to trial but with both sides having by then incurred significant legal costs.

The best initial advice that lawyers can give is for the parties to keep communicating and try to resolve the dispute themselves. Although we are always happy to act on behalf of a partner or the partnership, involving lawyers can escalate the dispute and start incurring significant costs. If it is not possible to avoid using lawyers then it is better to get them involved sooner rather than later (although we would say that). Getting lawyers involved early will help you with assessing the strength and risk involved in any claim, and therefore how to pursue or defend it, as well as how best to resolve the dispute while hopefully keeping costs proportional to the value of the claim itself.

PARTNERSHIP CHANGES – THE ACCOUNTANT'S PERSPECTIVE

Mike Gilbert

It is a fact of life that medical practices will frequently experience a change of partners, triggered by retirements or leaving for pastures new. This event has significant financial and administrative implications that we consider below and which practice managers need to be aware of.

Let us assume that in the fictitious practice of Upside Medical Practice, Dr Prodit retires on 31 March 2013, at which time Dr Preventit agrees to become a property owner and Dr Lancit is admitted to the partnership on immediate full parity and on a property-owning basis. The balance sheet of the practice at 31 March 2013 discloses the following:

	£	£
PARTNERS' FUNDS:		
Property capital accounts		85,100
Partners' current accounts		52,922
		138,022
EMPLOYMENT OF FUNDS:		
Tangible fixed assets		264,801
Loans		(174,900)
		89,901
CURRENT ASSETS:		
Stock of drugs	5,016	
Debtors and prepayments	108,732	
Cash at bank and in hand	92,397	
	206,145	
CURRENT LIABILITIES:		
Creditors and accrued charges	39,129	
Provision for income tax	118,895	
	158,024	
NET CURRENT ASSETS		
		48,121
		138,022

On further examination, the property capital accounts represent the equity in the property, being the value of £260,000 less loans of £174,900, being £85,100 divided as follows:

	Dr Prodit	Dr Pokit	Dr Treatit	Dr Curit	Dr Preventit	TOTAL
At 1 April 2012	15,425	15,425	15,425	15,425	–	61,700
Loans repaid in year	5,850	5,850	5,850	5,850	–	23,400
	£21,275	£21,275	£21,275	£21,275	–	£85,100

The partners' current accounts are disclosed as follows:

	Dr Prodit	Dr Pokit	Dr Treatit	Dr Curit	Dr Preventit	TOTAL
	£	£	£	£	£	£
At 1 April 2012	10,763	10,602	11,425	12,228	11,715	56,733
Net income for the year	133,825	126,851	127,139	128,029	121,339	637,183
	144,588	137,453	138,564	140,257	133,054	693,916
Monthly drawings	61,200	60,000	63,600	63,600	66,000	314,400
Equalisation	6,763	6,602	7,425	8,228	7,715	36,733
Seniority drawn	11,220	5,129	4,663	4,778	732	26,522
Class 2 NI contributions	111	111	111	111	111	555
Superannuation	7,589	7,634	7,311	7,264	7,116	36,914
Tax paid and provided	40,980	41,950	39,720	40,440	39,380	202,470
Loans repaid	5,850	5,850	5,850	5,850	–	23,400
	133,713	127,276	128,680	130,271	121,054	640,994
At 31 March 2013	10,875	10,177	9,884	9,986	12,000	52,922

Let us also assume that the practice obtained a professional valuation of the property under the partnership deed at 31 March 2013, which amounted to £300,000. We are now in a position to consider the financial options available to effect the buy-in and pay-out, which are:

1 Dealing first with the partners' current accounts, Dr Prodit needs to be paid £10,875 by the practice

2 So far as concerns Dr Lancit, he needs to pay into the practice approximately £10,000 to be on a par with the other partners. He can either achieve this by way of, say, a personal loan, or he could restrict his drawings by £400 per month for the first 25 months to catch up over a period of time. Incoming partners normally favour the latter approach but the matter is usually dictated by the practice cashflow

3 We can now turn to the surgery premises. Both Dr Preventit and Dr Lancit could take out personal loans of £25,020 each, pay the same into the practice and then Dr Prodit could withdraw £31,275, and the other continuing

partners could withdraw £6,255 each. This is best illustrated by plotting the movement of the property capital accounts as follows:

	Dr Prodit	Dr Pokit	Dr Treatit	Dr Curit	Dr Preventit	Dr Lancit	TOTAL
	£	£	£	£	£	£	£
At 31 March 2013	21,275	21,275	21,275	21,275	–	–	85,100
Revaluation	10,000	10,000	10,000	10,000	–	–	40,000
	31,275	31,275	31,275	31,275	–	–	125,100
Introduce	–	–	–	–	25,020	25,020	50,040
Withdraw	(31,275)	(6,255)	(6,255)	(6,255)	-	-	(50,040)
At 1 April 2013	–	25,020	25,020	25,020	25,020	25,020	125,100

In this way we now have five equal owners of the equity in the property, which is the value of £300,000 less loans of £174,900, being £125,100.

4   The practice must communicate with its lenders so that Dr Prodit is released from his obligations towards the property loan and Dr Preventit and Dr Lancit are 'signed up' to replace Dr Prodit in terms of the loan liability

5   So far as concerns taxation, the property transaction is a chargeable event for capital gains tax purposes, which will apply to Dr Prodit in disposing of his 25% interest and also to Drs Pokit, Treatit and Curit in disposing of their 5% interest each in the property, but the amount of tax involved to the latter is unlikely to be significant. Dr Preventit and Dr Lancit will obtain personal tax relief on the interest incurred on their personal loans

6   If Dr Preventit and Dr Lancit are reluctant to take out personal loans at this stage in their lives, then an alternative is to take out a practice loan of £50,040, which will become their total responsibility and leave their balances on the property capital account at exactly zero.

7   There is indeed a further approach available, achieved with the help of the practice lenders. It may be possible for the practice to take out a new loan of £125,100, which makes their total loans £300,000, being the exact value of the surgery premises. Obviously, if this occurs, the equity in the surgery premises becomes exactly zero. This route provides the practice with £125,100 cash, which can be distributed equally to Dr Prodit, Dr Pokit, Dr Treatit and Dr Curit, being £31,275 each. While Dr Prodit is liable to capital gains tax, the others are not because raising additional finance is not a chargeable event for capital gains tax purposes. The benefit of this approach is threefold:

a   Dr Prodit is paid out

b   Drs Pokit, Treatit and Curit release their own equity long before they otherwise might have anticipated c   Dr Preventit and Dr Lancit do not have to raise personal loans, but merely buy in by signing up to their 20% share each of the practice loans of £300,000.

The downside of this approach is that there is no longer any equity in the property and the £300,000 loans need to be serviced out of current practice earnings, particularly notional rent.

So much for the financial transaction at a partnership change. There are however other matters that practice managers need to be aware of and have to be dealt with on a partnership change. These can broadly be summarised as follows using the above example as a guide:

1   Cancel the direct debit in respect of Dr Prodit's Class 2 NI contributions
2   Advise the practice accountants of the partnership change so that Dr Lancit can properly be set up as self-employed and start paying Class 2 NI contributions (form CT41G). In this way the partnership tax return can be properly drawn up
3   Advise the practice solicitors of the partnership change so that the partnership deed can be suitably amended. Remember that if this is overlooked the existing partnership deed will be invalid
4   If Dr Prodit undertakes an outside appointment in practice time whereby the income earned is 'pooled', advise the customer of the retirement and the name of the partner taking over
5   Advise the primary care organisation and the NHS Pensions Agency, giving three months' notice of retirement of Dr Prodit. Advise both organisations of the pending admission of Dr Lancit into the partnership
6   Agree in advance with the primary care organisation that the existing GMS or PMS contract remains intact
7   Cancel any subscriptions paid by the practice on behalf of Dr Prodit, in particular the professional indemnity insurance
8   Advise any other relevant suppliers of the partnership change. If paid by the practice, this could of course relate to Dr Prodit's mobile phone, for example
9   Advise the practice insurers of the partnership change
10 Place notices in the reception area advising patients of the partnership change
11 See to changing the practice letterhead and any other relevant stationery
12 See to the amendment of all practice signs in and around the surgery premises
13 Ensure that all terms relating to an outgoing partner contained in the partnership deed are adhered to
14 Advise the practice solicitors to deal with the legal documents in connection with transferring the title to the property
15 In the absence of a partnership agreement, advise the practice solicitors to draw up a retirement deed

16 Determine level of drawings for Dr Lancit and remind him that the practice will save up for his income tax payments

17 If the practice is registered for VAT (normally dispensing practices) advise HMRC of the partnership change.

As can be seen, there is much to be done when there is a partnership change but it is worth getting it right if only to avoid an expensive and time-consuming partnership dispute some time in the future.

PARTNERSHIP CHANGES – THE LAWYER'S PERSPECTIVE

Oliver Pool

Retirement is easy. Recruitment is difficult. At least, that is the case as far as the legals go.

Retirement

Partners often talk about the need to sign a deed of retirement when they leave. However, if the practice has a proper partnership deed in place, there should be no need to incur the cost of drawing up a separate deed of retirement, because the partnership deed itself should contain the relevant provisions to cover the partner's retirement. If the existing partnership deed is sufficiently robust, then the involvement of a solicitor to deal with a retirement won't always be necessary – the departure can be dealt with simply by instructing the accountants to draw up a succession account, and paying out the retired partner in due course.

In our view one only needs a deed of retirement if there is no partnership deed, or if the partnership deed is insufficient for some reason, or if a particular change needs to be made to the terms of the partnership deed, perhaps because the deed also needs to deal with the settlement of a dispute between the partners.

It is worth mentioning two important provisions to look out for in partnership deeds. First, most deeds will provide that partners cannot retire at the same time. Once a partner has handed in his or her notice, this starts a 'freeze' period and no other partner can retire until the first one has finished his or her notice. This is to prevent partners leaving in quick succession, which can of course be extremely detrimental to the health of the practice. Of course, one cannot entirely prevent partners leaving (slavery having been abolished long ago), but this sort of provision does at least slow down the car crash, even if it cannot prevent it altogether.

Second, all partners close to retirement will be interested in what the partnership deed says about the return of their capital. Almost all deeds will set out in detail how the partner's share is calculated. Different practices take different approaches to when it must be paid by. And different lawyers take different approaches to what happens until payment is made.

In our view, the best way to avoid tension between the partners is to preserve the status quo as nearly as possible. We usually provide that, if a partner has retired but has not yet had his or her property capital returned, the fairest thing to do is to allow him or her a share of notional rent (less borrowing costs). One cannot of course call this notional rent as such – because notional rent can only be paid to someone who holds a Personal Medical Services (PMS) or General Medical Services (GMS) contract, and by definition the retired partner does not. However, our partnership deeds provide that interest equivalent to the notional rent, less borrowing costs that he or she always used to receive, continues to be paid to the partner until his or her capital is returned.

One difficulty that can arise with retired partners, and where a deed of retirement is often needed, is when they are allowed to retire from the partnership but continue to hold a share of the assets, usually of the surgery premises. This is a situation best avoided as it creates a whole range of potentially difficult issues. One major area for discussion is whether a lease is required between the property owners (now including a non-partner who is no longer party to the partnership agreement and so not bound by it) and the continuing GP practice.

Arguably, a periodic tenancy is created in this situation anyway, whether or not a written lease is put in place. We consider these issues further in the property Topics but, whatever approach is taken, it is an issue that requires careful consideration with full knowledge of the consequences of whatever action is taken.

Accession

There is a common misconception that partners who are 'on probation' or are serving a 'mutual assessment period' do not need to sign the partnership deed. This is wrong, and can be quite dangerous.

Probationary partners are full partners in a legal sense. Case law suggests that, when a new partner joins a practice without signing the deed, the existing partnership deed becomes unenforceable and the partnership becomes what is known as a 'partnership at will', which can be dissolved by any partner at any time. This is a situation worth avoiding, because if there were a dispute the partnership could be dissolved, which places the practice at risk of the practice contract going out to tender, bank funding being called in, and all staff becoming entitled to redundancy costs.

Put another way, there would be little legal right to ask an unsuccessful probationary partner to leave the practice until he or she had signed up to a partnership deed or deed of accession that contained provisions requiring him or her to leave when told to!

So the partnership deed should be signed, or amended, on or before the day a partner joins.

It is important to be clear about terms with a new partner right from the word go. If anything unusual or onerous is part of the deal, then that should be made clear during the recruitment process.

We take the view that it is for the good of the practice as a whole if all the partners are 'in the same boat' and have a share in all the assets. We don't necessarily say that all partners must have equal shares, or pro rata shares, but each partner ought to have a stake in all the assets of the business. The area where this is of most relevance is in relation to the surgery premises. Not all practices own their own freehold, but for those that do it is almost always the partnership's most valuable asset. We have seen many practices run into partnership disputes because some partners have an interest and others do not.

Ten years ago disputes would arise because the property owners were enjoying the notional rent income and would not allow newcomers to buy a share of the premises. These days the dispute is more often that new partners are reluctant to buy into the premises, perhaps because they are having trouble raising the capital or perhaps because they take a pessimistic view of the value of the asset in the long term.

It is for this reason that we strongly encourage practices who own their premises to be absolutely clear at interview time that one cannot be a partner at the practice without owning a share of the premises. Too often a practice is faced with a competent partner who is willing to join the practice but not to buy a share of the surgery, leaving the other partners with a difficult decision. The pressures are understandable, but we encourage partners not to permit this. Not only is it unjust to allow one partner to 'cherry pick' the assets he or she wants and leave those he or she doesn't, which itself may cause resentment, but it also indicates a lack of commitment to the practice on the part of the new partner. In our view allowing in non-property-owning partners is to store up troubles for the future.

With that in mind, practices that own their own freehold should be clear during recruitment that new partners will be expected to buy in. New partners should be required to sign a deed that binds them to buy in at the end of their probation, and this should be signed on or before their first day as a partner – you should not wait until the end of the probation.

PARTNERSHIP CHANGES – THE BANKER'S PERSPECTIVE

Ian Crompton

When partners change in partnership it is important to involve the practice accountants and solicitors, and to let the bank know.

There are many wider legal issues, which are covered in other sections, but it is important to recognise that a bank will assume the partners are those shown on the bank mandate, i.e. the agreement under which the bank accounts operate.

Partnership bank accounts usually involve joint and several liability; in simple terms this means if there is any borrowing all the partners in that partnership are responsible for the full amount. It is important to realise that if, for any reason, partner A cannot or does not uphold his or her obligation the remaining partner(s) are responsible for what may be considered A's share of the debt.

Should you be an exiting partner, it is therefore important that after you have agreed any partnership settlement pay-out etc. you should, along with the lawyers acting for the changes, make sure the bank account mandate is changed. This is so that you are not potentially responsible for debts incurred after you have left the partnership.

If you are joining a partnership you will normally be included on the bank account mandate. At this time you will become party to any new borrowing and will be 'jointly and severally' liable as outlined above.

It is important that within the changes the accountants and lawyers sort out who is responsible for 'old' loans. As a new partner you will not necessarily become liable for existing loans, i.e. those taken out before you arrived, unless you agree to it. Be clear what you are agreeing to and take independent legal advice as appropriate.

New partners are often asked to provide an amount of cash towards the working capital (i.e. the normal cash requirements) of the partnership. The accountants will work out how much is required and it is usually similar or the same as the amount being paid to the partner who is leaving. The amount will vary from practice to practice but may be (say) £20,000 to £40,000.

Most new partners do not have this cash readily to hand and therefore borrow it. Most banks are used to this sort of request and, while any bank can be used, it is likely that the bank that looks after the practice account will be keen to lend and provide fair rates.

Some accountants will recommend that partner buy-in loans are taken as 'interest only'; this is where the borrower only pays the interest and does not make any capital repayment, i.e. the loan amount does not reduce as with a repayment loan. Since 2007/8 some banks no longer offer interest-only options or, if they do, they may charge a 'premium', i.e. a slightly higher rate. It is worth shopping around if necessary, but it should be remembered that the loan has to be repaid at some time and, if the practice has incurred losses, the capital sum initially invested will not be there to clear the loan on retirement.

Partnership deeds – the accountant's perspective

Mike Gilbert

The need for a partnership agreement must now be clear to all GPs and practice managers. Without one there is a 'partnership at will', which means that relations between partners are governed by the Partnership Act 1890. This is rightly deemed to be an unstable business relationship, if for no other reason than the partnership can be dissolved at any time.

There are many legal and administrative issues that need to be dealt with in the partnership agreement, but this topic is focused on the important financial issues that need to be considered by way of best practice. The suggestions made are for guidance only and partners of course have the right to make whatever decisions they wish, provided they are legally enforceable.

The important variables and essential clauses so far as concerns finance are deemed to be as follows:

1. Partnership capital

This is normally defined as the total assets less total liabilities of the practice, being the net worth of the practice on the balance sheet date. The net worth can be split between property capital accounts (representing the equity in the surgery premises) and partners' current accounts (representing the value of all other assets less liabilities). The partners have to decide in what proportion the surgery premises will be owned. Separately they need to decide in what proportion the other assets less liabilities will be owned, although this is normally on the basis of profit shares. It is not uncommon for partners to specify a fixed amount that must be retained in the partners' current accounts in order to finance the running of the practice (working capital).

2. Rights of occupation

If there is a partner in the practice who is not a property owner, then the other partners may wish to grant him or her a licence to occupy the premises while he or she remains a partner in the practice. Such a licence might avoid the problems inherent with a formal lease in terms of sitting tenants and possible restriction on notional rent received.

3. Interest

The partners need to agree the rate, if any, of interest payable on the balance retained in the partners' current accounts. Normally, this does not apply, but every practice is different. However, when a partner leaves and is entitled to a pay-out, interest should perhaps be charged from the anniversary of the succession date.

4. Shares of profits

The partners have to decide in what proportion they are going to divide practice profits. This is normally done on the basis of sessions worked, but other methods can of course be employed. However, the partners may decide that there are 'prior' shares and charges to be allocated to individual partners. Typically, this will include notional rent and loan interest if the property is held in different proportions from the profit-sharing ratio. It will also include employers' superannuation contributions paid, and may include such items as seniority and work performed outside practice hours.

5. Partnership vs. private income

It is quite common for the partnership agreement to include a clause which states that all work performed in practice time is included as 'pooled' partnership income. It follows that work performed outside practice time is specifically allocated to the individual partner, but with express permission of the other partners and provided that it does not have a detrimental effect on partnership work. In this context out-of-hours work is particularly relevant.

In this section the partners should decide upon how to deal with legacies and gifts. Finally, the partners should agree on how to apportion quality aspiration and achievement payments – normally, this would be on a straight-apportionment basis, which means an end-year apportionment in the same proportion as the partnership share, reduced by the number of days missing from the full year in question.

6. Expenses

In a similar way the partners should agree on what expenses are to be met by the partnership, what expenses are to be met personally, and what partnership expenses are to be prior charged to individual partners. Typically, the expenses deemed to be met by the individual partner include motor expenses, spouse's salary, home and mobile telephones, courses and conferences, locum insurance, subscriptions, and personal accountancy fees. Strictness in this respect may not be best practice; being reasonable with one another inevitably results in the most appropriate solution. It is not uncommon to include in this clause a requirement for partners to complete their personal expenses return by a certain date in order to prevent the hold-up of the practice accounts and calculations of the tax liabilities.

7. Superannuation

The calculation of superannuation contributions and superannuable income is based on the taxable income of each and every GP after eliminating the 'profit' relating to non-NHS work. Thus, the taxable income can include profit share, private income, and prior shares of profit for each GP, together with their attributable share of partnership expenses, personal expenses, and prior charges of profit. It follows therefore that the contributions of GPs in a practice will almost certainly not be in normal profit-sharing ratio, and accordingly the partnership agreement may state that the employer's contributions should be prior charged to each relevant partner, and employee's contributions should be charged on an individual basis to the partners' current accounts. In this way, no one partner is subsidising the pension provision of another.

8. NHS contract

The partnership agreement should refer to the holding of the General Medical Services (GMS) or Personal Medical Services (PMS) contract and deal with each partner's obligations in this respect in terms of performer's lists and the like.

9. Leasehold premises

The partnership agreement should refer to the partners' obligations towards the lease and how they may be released from them on leaving the practice. The partners may decide to create a 'sinking fund' in order to meet their liabilities under the dilapidation clause of the lease so that the potential cost is spread over all partners on a time-apportioned basis. This should include a notional tax adjustment so that the tax relief would also be spread on a time-apportioned basis.

10. Professional advisers

In simplicity, the partnership agreement should state who the practice bankers, accountants and solicitors are. So far as concerns the bankers it is important to state clearly who the cheque signatories are.

11. Insurances

It is not uncommon for a partnership agreement to contain a requirement for partners to personally have certain insurances in place. If the practice does not pay for indemnity insurance then it is essential the partners obtain it at their own expense. Some agreements ask for partners to maintain a certain level of life assurance so that, in the event of a partner's death, his or her family does not become a burden on the practice. The most common clause relates to locum insurance, which partners may be required to take out. This 'kicks in' after a specific period of absence, maybe 13 or perhaps 26 weeks.

12. Absence

This normally relates to periods of sickness, maternity and paternity leave, or compassionate leave, but can also relate to absence due to jury service, educational courses, sabbaticals, suspension and service in the armed forces. The partners have to decide when the practice should be responsible for the cost of locum cover and for how long. It is not uncommon for a practice to pay for a sickness locum for a period of 13 or 26 weeks, after which the cost becomes a liability for the sick partner. It is important that the locum insurance policy should match such a decision. The same decision has to be made regarding maternity and paternity leave.

13. Taxation

Income tax is not a joint and several liability of the partnership but a personal liability of the individual partners. However, the practice needs to appoint a 'nominated' partner for taxation purposes who will be responsible for signing the partnership tax return on behalf of the partnership. This can be an onerous role as the personal expenses of all the partners are included in the partnership tax return. To avoid HMRC attacking the nominated partner for any defalcations, the partnership agreement should include an indemnity for the nominated partner whereby the other partners would indemnify him or her for any such defalcations.

14. Outgoing partners

The issue of an outgoing partner can arise on death, retirement or merely by leaving the practice. On leaving, an outgoing partner is entitled to his or her share of the worth of the practice within a specified time period. This represents the balance on his or her property capital account plus the balance on his or her current account. If the departure is on the year-end accounting date it is not unreasonable to expect the information to be available and payment made within one year. However, if a departure is not on a year-end accounting date it is normal to await the preparation of the accounts to the next usual accounting date and time-apportion the profits during the year. Given that this may create a delay, it is not unusual for the agreement to state that interest will accrue from the first anniversary of the departure date.

An incoming partner cannot be bound by the partnership agreement drawn up by the other partners until he or she becomes a party to it. Consequently, it is up to the continuing partners to buy out the outgoing partner's share. This is normally achieved in the partnership agreement by providing the continuing partners with an option to acquire the outgoing partner's share. This should not be an obligation as it could have a detrimental effect so far as concerns inheritance tax. In practice, unless there is a major dispute, the continuing partners will take up the option.

The other issue to be covered in the partnership agreement is the question of valuations. Frankly, with the exception of surgery premises, all other assets and liabilities should be taken at book value to save the cost of pointless revaluation. So far as concerns surgery premises, the agreement should require a professional independent valuation to be undertaken on the basis of both market value and an existing use value, taking account of notional rent received. The nature of the premises determines which of these valuations is most appropriate. For those GPs undertaking major new surgery development it may be necessary to include a clause which states that the value to be used will be the higher of cost or valuation. Otherwise, it is doubtful whether any GP over the age of 45 would wish to be involved in a major new development for the fear of negative equity. In this way, the worst that could happen to an outgoing partner would be to depart on the basis of no profit, no loss.

As can be seen there is much to be considered when drafting a partnership agreement from a financial point of view. Practices are advised to use solicitors who are experienced in the process and involve their accountants in drafting the financial terms. Further partnership advice can be obtained from the British Medical Association, who provide a detailed drafting service.

Partnership deeds – the lawyer's perspective

Oliver Pool

A surprisingly large number of GP partnerships don't have partnership deeds in place. A larger number still think they do, but in fact have a document that is not binding. This presents a number of problems for those practices. First, it places them in breach of their Personal Medical Services (PMS) or General Medical Services (GMS) contract, which obliges them to have a partnership deed in place. The Care Quality Commission also makes it a condition of registration to have an up-to-date and enforceable partnership deed, on the basis that it is a simple matter of good governance. Second, though, not having a partnership deed can prove very costly indeed for a practice in the event of a dispute.

A partnership without an enforceable deed in place is subject to any of the following scenarios:

No enforceable partnership deed almost certainly means no right to expel a partner. This means you could be stuck in partnership with someone who has behaved very improperly but refuses to retire without a pay-off.

It may well be impossible to enforce a probationary period against a new partner. If the partnership wanted him or her to leave at the end of the probation period, the new partner (who, after all, has nothing to lose) may refuse and require a pay-off. The new partner would have the practice 'over a barrel' in this situation because the new partner is in a position to dissolve the practice on notice – for more of which, see below.

If there is no partnership deed, there is no agreement as to locum costs. This can mean that a partner can go off sick (or can claim to go off sick), with the partnership having to pick up all the locum costs until such time as a departure can be negotiated.

With no partnership deed in place there is no certainty as to what the 'rules' are, and this in itself makes a dispute more likely. Are decisions taken by majority or is unanimity required? How much holiday is someone entitled to? When is someone entitled to a return of his or her capital? The list goes on and on.

As mentioned above, if the practice has no enforceable partnership deed, any partner can dissolve the practice at any time, merely by giving notice. This is a disaster scenario, and one to be avoided at all costs, because on dissolution:

- the PMS or GMS contract comes to an end, and may well have to be put out to tender, even if the practice remains a functioning unit. The remaining partners then have the cost and stress of having to win their own contract back, and they will not necessarily be successful if commercial operators make a bid
- all the staff may well become entitled to redundancy payments
- any bank funding can be called in immediately – this applies to partnership mortgages just as much as to overdrafts, which could place the practice in a very difficult situation.

There is, of course, a large amount of detail in a partnership deed on which this topic could focus, but we limit ourselves here to two issues of current interest – how to deal with premises issues and how to deal with sickness absence and locum insurance.

A separate property deed?

Many solicitors encourage partnerships who own the freehold of their premises to draw up two separate documents, one dealing with the medical partnership and a second property-owning partnership deed, or deed of trust, setting out the rules relating to the property. In our view, provided that the premises is treated as a partnership asset in the accounts, there is no need for two separate documents. One might suggest two separate documents if the partners explicitly wish to take the premises 'off the books', and leave it as an investment for the property owners, who will retain it into retirement. However, if the premises is a partnership asset then it can be dealt with in the partnership deed (even if not all of the partners have bought into the building). This is far simpler and cheaper than having two separate documents.

Sickness absence and locum insurance

Some practices do not have an overall locum insurance policy in place, instead leaving it up to individual partners to arrange their own policies, or not to do so if they see fit. The partners are entitled to adopt this approach if they wish. However, we generally advise practices that they should strongly consider having a partnership policy in place. This is for two main reasons:

- first, if a partner has an expensive lifestyle and does not keep up his or her own policy, then when this partner is off sick the other partners are placed in the invidious position of making him or her pay locum costs. The result is, for example, that the partner becomes unable to pay the mortgage. This places a lot of 'moral' pressure on the other partners not to enforce the payment of locum costs, even though the fault does not lie with them at all
- second, it is increasingly common that, when partners go off sick, some or all of the others feel they are not justified in doing so. This can lead

to the other partners pursuing a course of action, or making comments, that later result in claims for discrimination on the grounds of disability. When locum insurance is in place, this is less of a problem; however, when there is no insurance (so the other partners are bearing the financial cost as well as the disruption) it can really 'raise the temperature', making a discrimination claim all the more likely.

It is worth stressing that if you have a practice-based locum insurance policy the provider will almost always break down the cost of insuring each partner, so that you can set it against share of profits, if you wish to.

Suspension

Partnerships are naturally concerned as to what happens in the event of a partner being suspended. It is important to remember that suspended partners have not been found guilty of anything, and suspension can happen to anyone who is quite innocent – it is not the same as being struck off, and should not be thought of in the same way.

Our suggestion is that a partner who is suspended should continue to receive his or her usual drawings until he or she is either struck off or reinstated. This should not in fact mean a financial burden for the partnership, because the Statement of Financial Entitlements (SFE) obliges NHS England to reimburse a suspended partner's locum costs, provided he or she is still entitled to at least 90% of his or her usual drawings. Under the SFE 2013 reimbursement of such costs was capped at around £1,500 per week.

NHS England has suggested that it no longer wishes to reimburse practices during periods of suspension. Nonetheless, the law remains that the SFE as it currently stands obliges NHS England to make that reimbursement. If a practice were to change its partnership agreements so as to make locum costs the expense of a suspended partner, all it would achieve is to save NHS England the need to reimburse, at the cost of the suspended partner. Until the SFE changes, we recommend not following this course of action.

INCORPORATION – TO BE OR NOT TO BE – THE ACCOUNTANT'S PERSPECTIVE

Mike Gilbert

We are frequently asked about the appropriateness of forming a limited liability company (LLC) to meet contractual obligations or indeed private work. So far as concerns the latter, the combination of corporation tax and tax on dividend income is normally no cheaper than paying income tax, and would therefore only be of benefit to a GP who has no immediate need of drawing the income. However, there may be an opportunity to involve other family members if properly set up with obvious tax savings. Furthermore, if the income is derived from an NHS source, there may be savings in terms of superannuation contributions if the company does not qualify as an employing authority for pension purposes.

In summary, the pros and cons of incorporating private work are as follows:

	Pro	Con
Limited liability protection	✓	
Tax saving if no immediate requirement for funds	✓	
Tax saving if family members involved	✓	
No National Insurance on dividends	✓	
Potential saving in superannuation contributions	✓	
Compliance with Companies Act		✓
Accounts on public record		✓
Tax if family members not involved		✓
Formation and administration costs		✓

So far as concerns surgery premises, we do not normally recommend the use of an LLC for a number of reasons as follows:

- the premises are 'locked' into the company
- capital allowances are not available to the individuals, only to the company itself

- notional and other rents may need to increase sufficiently to enable the company to pay dividends in order to finance the borrowing of incoming partners, and may not be fully reimbursed
- the need to create a formal lease, which leads to a stamp duty land tax cost.

If risk is an issue, then the formation of a limited liability partnership (LLP) may be an option to consider from the property point of view.

Can you use LLCs to run General Medical Services (GMS), Personal Medical Services (PMS) and Alternative Provider Medical Services (APMS) contracts? The following is a breakdown of practices in England at 30 September 2013. The total number of practices is 7,962 of which:

	Traditional	Limited company
GMS	4,339	6
PMS	3,197	12
APMS	173	98
PCTMS	137	–
	7,846	116

This means that only 1.3% of practices are limited companies, which must surely tell its own story. It must be borne in mind particularly that most companies are owned by private providers with APMS contracts.

Nevertheless, the following table sets out the legal position as we understand it, showing who can and who cannot hold contracts:

	GMS	PMS	APMS
Individual general medical practitioners	✓	✓	✓
NHS employees	✗	✓	✓
Individuals who are not GPs or NHS employees	✗	✗	✓
Medical partnerships	✓	✗	✓
Limited liability partnerships	✗	✗	✓
Companies limited by shares owned by GPs and NHS family	✓	✓	✓
Other limited liability companies, public or private	✗	✗	✓
Companies limited by guarantee	✗	✗	✓
Industrial and provident societies, friendly societies, voluntary organisations, etc.	✗	✗	✓
Companies where there are disqualified directors	✗	✗	✗

What about a corporate partner? The answer is no for a GMS contract and yes for an APMS contract. So far as concerns PMS the answer is yes if it meets the necessary criteria – the contract is held by individuals. For this purpose a company is regarded as an individual. The advantage of a corporate partner is twofold:

- shares can be held by employees and other members of the NHS family
- the partners could benefit from a saving in superannuation contributions and thereby avoid breaching the annual allowance and lifetime allowance for taxation purposes.

Specialist medical accountants need to work closely with specialist medical independent financial advisers when advising on the use of companies for tax and superannuation planning. This is because of the knock-on effect to final pension and tax-free lump sum entitlements.

A word of warning is required regarding the use of corporate partners. HMRC is now attacking profit-and-loss allocation schemes where the overall effect is to transfer profit between entities subject to different tax rules in a way that reduces the overall liability to tax. It considers that the use of a limited company as a partner is an abusive manipulation of profit to achieve a tax advantage and have legislated accordingly.

Finally, it is worth pointing out that there is no mechanism to transfer any contract. While a GMS contract could be held by a limited company, the contract cannot be transferred seamlessly and the practice risks the NHS Commissioning Board (NCB) putting the contract out to tender. A PMS contract would typically be moved by introducing a limited company as a partner. Then, after a period, typically 28 days, the other partners retire, leaving the contract solely in the hands of the company. However, NCB approval would be required to vary the contract to introduce a partner and may not be granted.

So, to be or not to be? Limited companies can have their use but at the present time the circumstances when they would be appropriate is severely limited. Anyone considering making use of a company should seek specialist advice from both lawyers and accountants who understand the NHS contract and superannuation implications.

INCORPORATION – THE BANKER'S PERSPECTIVE

Ian Crompton

It is increasingly common for businesses to 'incorporate' and start to trade through a limited company. This is often on accountant's advice and may involve either a part, such as the property ownership, or all of the business moving across to a limited company. In the case of GPs this may be the provision of new services taken on under the new Any Qualified Provider (AQP) procedures. A bank will be happy to operate a limited company account but there are some important considerations.

First, there will need to be agreement as to who operates the account, i.e. who signs cheques, agrees overdrafts, etc. This will all be documented in a new account mandate. There will also need to be the normal identification procedures completed for all the main parties, and this could take some time if there are lots of people involved. Remember also that whenever there is a change in who runs the account there will be a need to involve the bank and update the mandates.

INCORPORATION AND OTHER LEGAL STRUCTURES – THE LAWYER'S PERSPECTIVE

Oliver Pool

At time of writing the vast majority of GP practices have not incorporated – most are either single-handers or normal partnerships. Many other professions, including lawyers, have started to become limited liability partnerships (LLPs), but this has not been the case with GP practices for several reasons.

An LLP cannot hold a Personal Medical Services (PMS) or General Medical Services (GMS) contract. Neither can it be an 'employing authority' for the purposes of the NHS pension scheme – the effect of which is that a practice which became an LLP could place its staff outside the scheme – a costly mistake! So effectively it is currently off limits for a GP practice to put its core contract into an LLP.

The same does not go for limited companies, which can be employing authorities and can hold GMS or PMS contracts, provided they are properly constituted and (broadly speaking) are owned by those within the 'NHS family'. However, a partnership of GPs cannot simply opt to place its existing GMS contract in the name of a new company they run. This is because, like all NHS contracts, GMS/PMS contracts are non-assignable, i.e. they cannot be assigned without the consent of NHS England.

The GPs would have to ask the Local Area Team (LAT) of NHS England nicely whether they could transfer the contract. However, the LAT's response is likely to be along the lines that they cannot take the contract away from the partners and give it to the company; instead they would have to run a tender process to ensure that the company is the best 'person' to give the contract to. The benefits of incorporation are usually dwarfed by the risks and costs of a tender process!

This being so, most practices are reasonably comfortable to remain unincorporated. In a traditional partnership, the partners have unlimited joint and several liability for the business as a whole, but they usually feel they can live with this given that they have comprehensive insurance against clinical risk, a guaranteed (albeit tightening!) income stream, and reimbursement of notional rent.

This does not mean, however, that no GPs are involved with limited companies or even LLPs. In another part of the book (see pp. 72–5) we discuss GP federations and provider companies. However, practices will often run companies in their own right.

GPs may set up other non-core business – such as an occupational health practice or a minor surgery unit – which is clearly outside the scope of their GMS work. There are various reasons why one may want to put this work into a separate legal vehicle. One such reason is the operation of 'the goodwill rules'.

The goodwill rules prevent GPs buying or selling goodwill in a GP practice – historically this is because the goodwill belongs to the state. It was purchased from GPs in 1948, and the NHS retains the benefit of it, so GPs are not allowed to try to sell it themselves. Thus, when a partner retires it is common practice to provide in a partnership deed that he or she is not paid anything for any goodwill in the practice, even if the partner started it from scratch and turned it single-handedly into a flourishing business. The retiring partner is entitled to no more than the value of the tangible assets he or she is handing over.

However, the goodwill rules only apply to core GMS and PMS income. Thus, a partner or partners setting up an occupational health practice or minor surgery unit may well wish to do so via a limited company. If this becomes a valuable business they will be able to sell the goodwill in it for value when they come to retire, in which case it will be helpful not to have it 'mixed up' with the PMS/GMS practice.

Setting up separate vehicles also brings with it the benefit of limited liability. On the other hand it means a separate Care Quality Commission registration, so the benefits and drawbacks should be considered each time.

ROLES AND RESPONSIBILITIES OF A COMPANY DIRECTOR

Scott McKenzie

Overview

Directors are appointed on behalf of shareholders to manage the business and run the day-to-day affairs of the company.

They have the powers to take business decisions and they are accountable to the shareholders and other stakeholders.

SEVEN STATUTORY REQUIREMENTS FOR DELIVERY OF DIRECTORS' DUTIES (COMPANIES ACT 2006)

- To act within powers granted within the Memorandum and Articles of Association of the company for the benefit of its shareholders.
- To promote the success of the company.
- To exercise independent judgement.
- To exercise reasonable care, skill and diligence.
- To avoid conflicts of interest.
- Not to accept benefits from third parties.
- To declare interests in proposed transactions or arrangements with the company.

See below for further information on these requirements.

SPECIFIC RESPONSIBILITIES

- Filing documents at Companies House, including annual return, report and accounts, changes of registered office, appointment/cessation of directors' terms of office.
- Keeping proper accounting records.
- Ensuring correct amount of taxation, VAT and National Insurance are paid, and paid on time.
- Compliance with employment law.
- Compliance with health and safety requirements.
- Ensuring financial viability.
- Being wary of legal pitfalls including data protection, defamation, libel and providing misleading information.

Liability of directors

If directors fail to carry out their duties with appropriate care and attention they could be jointly and severally liable for any resultant losses.

SEVEN STATUTORY REQUIREMENTS FOR DELIVERY OF DIRECTORS' DUTIES

1. Duty to act within powers awarded as director

The directors have the power to deal with any particular matter unless legislation or the company's own constitution direct otherwise.

Most companies do not have special constitutional arrangements to restrict the directors' powers, so the reality is that in most companies the directors can make any decision.

2. Duty to promote the success of the company

When making decisions the following non-exhaustive list of factors should be considered:

- long-term consequence of the decisions
- interests of employees
- relationship with suppliers and customers
- impact of the decision on the community and the environment
- desirability of maintaining a reputation for high standards of business conduct
- need to act fairly as between members of the company.

It will be difficult to balance these requirements one against another in some situations. It is important for the board to record the considerations that led to those decisions.

3. Duty to exercise independent judgement

Often duties are delegated but directors carry overall responsibility. This imposes a duty on a director of a company to exercise independent judgement.

A director will not be in breach of his or her duty if the director has exercised his or her own judgement in deciding whether to follow someone else's judgement on a matter.

4. Duty to exercise reasonable care, skill and diligence

Guidance explains this as that which would be exercised by a reasonably diligent person with:

1 The general knowledge, skill and experience that may be reasonably expected of a person carrying out the functions of a director in relation to the company (minimum duty owed); AND

2 The general knowledge, skill and experience that the director in fact possesses (level duty in consideration of a director's own level of experience and knowledge).

Therefore a director who has more experience, knowledge and skill will have a higher threshold in discharging his or her duty.

5. Duty to avoid conflicts of interest

A conflict of interest may occur when a director has an interest that might compromise his or her ability to carry out the role or job in a reliable way. Examples of such conflicts include favouring known suppliers or use of privileged information that may put particular suppliers at an advantage.

Directors have a duty to act in the best interests of the company. It is sensible to set up a process for declaring conflicts of interests. Consideration should also be given to any interest of those persons who hold multiple directorships.

6. Duty not to accept benefits from third parties

A director is not permitted to accept a benefit from a third party by reason of his or her being a director or doing or not doing anything as a director. Benefits cover both monetary and non-monetary. A director will not be in breach of this duty if the acceptance of such a benefit does not result in a conflict of interest.

Directors may need to take advice in this area if they are unsure.

7. Duty to declare interest in proposed transaction or arrangement with the company

Disclosure extends to a person connected with the director.

This issue most commonly arises in the following non-exhaustive list of situations:

- loans made by the company to a director or vice versa
- purchases from entities connected with a director
- sales made to entities connected with a director.

Practice mergers – beware the pitfalls – the accountant's perspective

Mike Gilbert

The number of practices in the UK fell from 9,906 on 30 September 2012 to 9,771 on 30 September 2013, while the number of GPs remained fairly constant. Thus, the obvious conclusion is that the loss of 135 practices is due to merger activity. But what, if any, are the attractions of a practice merger? The following reasons are often attributed to merger activity:

- the age profile of GPs discloses that there are more GPs aged over 50 than ever before, while at the other end entry into medical school and the number of registrars is at an all-time low. It is now difficult to recruit salaried GPs and locums, let alone partners. This recruitment crisis encourages smaller practices to seek merger in order to provide GP cover for patients
- some GPs believe that by merging practices it gives them a better chance of bidding successfully for contracts for enhanced services
- the pursuit of economies of scale in that cost savings will be made. Also, succession problems might be solved, particularly if surgery ownership is involved
- saving in administration time
- a belief that many practices will soon become unsustainable if they rely solely on the core contract.

The question is how much of the above is true given that previous activity has identified significant pitfalls with the process. Let us therefore consider the above items in the context of experience to date.

The first issue to consider is that there are hardly any practices in the UK with over six partners in the top 10% of GP earners. One has to remember that GPs receive no business training at medical school and medical practice is a 'business'. The bigger the practice the more difficult it is to manage it, and the formalities of business that need to be followed do not come easy to most GPs.

One can understand why the recruitment crisis drives some GPs to merger, but this may not be the only solution to the problem. It is possible for a 'federation' of practices to work together to deal with GP cover. In these circumstances, given that the federation is a separate legal entity, practices can remain independent and retain their own characteristics.

The argument that merger can provide better bidding power lacks conviction. The key issue in the bidding process is population coverage and most mergers will still not provide this ingredient. Clinical Commissioning Groups and Foundation Trusts seem to be keen to issue one contract per service and are loath to issue multiple contracts. This means that even the largest of practices may struggle in the bidding process. Again, 'federations' may provide the answer as they will have population coverage, and the work can be subcontracted to individual practices.

The economies of scale argument, i.e. cost savings, may have some merit but probably not in the short term. Practices should not identify staff savings (redundancies) prior to or during the merger process as to do so could lead to the employment tribunal. Rather, staff reduction should not be looked at until the merged practice is well under way, probably after six months at the earliest. Moreover, a merger can only solve a succession problem if recruitment becomes an impossibility. But beware – there is no guarantee that a merged practice will acquire surgery premises.

A saving in administration time may or may not occur depending upon how well the new merged practice is managed.

Given recent contract changes, it is right to question whether certain smaller practices will remain sustainable, particularly those that rely upon the Minimum Practice Income Guarantee (MPIG). However, practices have to consider whether federation would be a better option to follow than merger. Every case is different but great care needs to be taken in finding the right solution.

Sadly, there are even more pitfalls to consider. NHS England has to be brought into the equation to ensure that the core contracts of both practices are protected. Normally, it is easiest to merge two General Medical Services (GMS) practices, but the situation is more complex if both or one of the practices have a Personal Medical Services (PMS) contract. The protection of the core contract must be dealt with at the outset of merger negotiations, otherwise a great deal of time can be wasted.

There is yet another potential pitfall that can often be overlooked by practices and this concerns taxation. Where both parties to the merger have a year end of 31 March then there is no problem. However, where one or both of the parties to the merger have a year end other than 31 March then a problem can occur. The selection of accounting date can be crucial because, without care, the overlap tax time bomb (see pp. 14–16) can be triggered, which has the effect of accelerating tax payments.

The overall message is clear. Practices should seek specialist legal and accountancy advice early in the process, not only to ensure that the merger itself makes business sense, but also in order to avoid the many pitfalls along the way.

PRACTICE MERGERS – THE BANKER'S PERSPECTIVE

Ian Crompton

Lloyds Bank Commercial Banking's latest Healthcare Confidence Index shows that as many as 46% of GPs are now ready to retire, indicating that succession planning must be a key focus within the healthcare sector in the short-term future.

Coupled with confidence among GPs remaining low, and many of those surveyed indicating a desire to leave the profession, questions are being raised about the future of the sector, and the ways we can act to increase confidence and allow it to thrive going forward.

Government cuts clearly impact on the outlook for GPs, and it's a fine balance between handling busy waiting rooms while falling into line with the financial constraints that are in effect.

The change in the industry landscape is reflected in the attitude of GPs, with 90% of those responding to the survey expressing their belief that mergers, co-locations and larger multi-GP practices will become commonplace in the years to come, replacing traditional single-handed sites.

Although mergers seem to be the assumed way forward it is important that GPs consider all the reasons and implications for doing so. The reasoning is often due to 'synergies' or 'cost savings from efficiencies', but what does this really mean and how will it be achieved?

Saving costs in many businesses can mean closing premises or reducing the number of staff employed. If this is the case there needs to be a clear plan and understanding from all the parties involved. If there are no cost savings why is the merger taking place? Are there benefits to patients or employees? There may be many reasons but it is important to be clear and confident that all parties involved will understand the plan; do not do it just because everyone else seems to be doing so.

When considering a merger practices should consider all the financial and legal implications. It is recommended that a 'merger team' is brought together involving specialist accountants, solicitors and funding providers. These specialists should have experience not only of the sector but also of other mergers. They should be able to support GPs through the plans with appropriate understanding, while also dealing with any uncertainties.

It is essential to recognise that it is unlikely that profitability will be identical in all the practices planning to merge. Capital accounts will likely be different and there may be different agreements on sharing certain lines of income and drawings. All these issues need to be discussed and agreements reached that all parties can settle on, and a specialist accountant can help support these discussions.

The merging partners may already have agreements in place and a solicitor will need to work these together to produce a single binding partnership agreement that is acceptable to all parties. Specialist solicitors will know what topics need to be covered including drawings, valuations, working arrangements and retirements, and they can also help ensure that any NHS contracts are transferred effectively.

The banking arrangements should simply follow on from the discussions over finances and partnership agreements. If finance is required a bank will want to check suitable planning has been undertaken and partnership agreements and contractual transfers are in hand.

Banks will suggest accountants' advice is followed on the mergers and this will often involve a new partnership account being opened to run alongside the existing accounts. This will involve new bank mandates and there will need to be agreement on who signs on the new merged practice's behalf moving forward. Any borrowing on the new account, either temporary through the merger process or in the future, will be the responsibility of the new partners.

Each merger will be different and invariably none will be simple. The main recommendation is to plan early and seek advice and support from specialists, and a bank with a specialist healthcare team is the ideal choice for medical professionals to turn to during this kind of process.

Combining a relationship-focused banking experience with primary care experience, this type of dedicated banking service ensures the correct levels of advice, expertise and support to help healthcare businesses to thrive – whatever the social and economic climate.

PRACTICE MERGERS – THE LAWYER'S PERSPECTIVE

Oliver Pool and Ben Willis

Mergers have become increasingly common over the past five years or so. They are driven by various factors such as pressure on income, attempts to create economies of scale, the difficulty of recruitment of willing partners, and succession planning.

The legal structure of a merger

On a merger of two partnerships, one partnership (let's call it partnership A) will dissolve. The partners of partnership A will join the other partnership (let's call it partnership B), and take their assets across with them to partnership B.

This means that the merger itself can be effected simply by drawing up a new partnership agreement for partnership B (i.e. the newly merged partnership). This new partnership agreement can also contain the provisions necessary to capture the merger deal.

Once the merger takes place, all the partners become jointly and severally liable for all liabilities of both practices. While this may be 'fair' going forward, our approach is usually to recommend that indemnities are included against historic liabilities – so the 'A' partners will indemnify the 'B' partners against any liabilities that were in the 'A' partnership before the merger date – and vice versa.

As an example, the effect of these indemnities might be to protect the 'A' partners against an ongoing employment tribunal claim against the 'B' partners', or to protect the 'B' partners against a problem in the 'A' partners' accounts.

Dissolution of partnership A

The dissolution of partnership A means that the employees of partnership A will transfer by TUPE into partnership B and will therefore have a new employer. We discuss this in more detail below.

When partnership A dissolves, all its contracts come to an end. Technically this includes the General Medical Services (GMS) contract. There is a risk that the Local Area Team (LAT) could take the position that the contract should not just transfer to partnership A, but instead should be put out to tender. Generally this is only a theoretical risk, and we at VWV have never seen a Primary Care Trust (PCT) or a LAT do this, but the point remains. Given the importance of the practice contract, it is best to be careful on the matter. Reassurance should be sought from NHS England at an early stage, as it often takes a while to process.

Dissolution of a partnership also means that its bank funding can be called in immediately – or if a loan is in place at a favourable rate, the bank may exercise its right to renegotiate that rate. It is therefore important to involve the bank early on and to check whether it is likely to seek to take this sort of action. If either practice is changing banks it is more important to bear in mind, as one bank will be losing out and may therefore be less inclined to take a helpful approach.

Which of the two practices the partners decide to dissolve will depend on all the above. It is often the case that the smaller practice dissolves. However, if the smaller practice has a lot of bank borrowing or is changing banks, or has 'difficult' employees who may object to a transfer, or if NHS England has indicated it would be unwilling to transfer the smaller practice's contract, then it might make sense to dissolve the larger practice instead.

Due diligence exercise

It is very important that both practices keep their accountants involved throughout the merger, not least because the equalisation of profits is often a key block to a merger taking place, and the accountants will need to advise on this. If partners' profits do not equalise within three years of the merger then there could be a deemed breach of the goodwill rules (see p. 58).

Often in a merger of other types of businesses an extensive legal due diligence process is carried out, so that both businesses have a good idea of what risks and problems lie in the business they are merging into – i.e. the solicitors are asked to trawl through the businesses' commercial contracts etc. and produce a report. This is generally not required in a GP practice merger, and the cross-indemnities referred to above are generally sufficient. In VWV's experience due diligence in mergers of GP practices is limited to the accountants doing financial due diligence.

Employment issues

TUPE will apply to the merger due to the dissolution of practice A, and will operate to transfer the employees of practice A into practice B. Liabilities can arise if the proper process is not followed.

The employees who transfer will do so on their current terms and conditions, with their continuity of employment preserved. TUPE contains specific provisions regarding changing terms and conditions of employment of the transferring employees (including harmonisation of terms with the existing workforce) and dismissing employees.

TUPE also provides for a process of informing and consulting with affected employees (who may be employees of partnership B as well as partnership A) about the transfer and any measures that will take place as a consequence of the transfer (e.g. changes to pay dates).

Part of the reason behind the merger may be to save money by sharing staff and reducing staff numbers. The more change there is likely to be, and the more such 'measures' are envisaged, the more obligations to inform and consult both practices will have to be undertaken. However, if no measures are envisaged, the consultation process can be quite 'light touch'.

In any case, during the early stages of planning, it is worth avoiding putting anything about specific individuals' redundancies in any business plans or other written documents. If these were to come to light it could be used by anyone who has been made redundant as evidence that a fair process was not followed.

Property issues

The property interests of the two merging practices need to be carefully considered, especially if all assets and liabilities are to be 'pooled'. Some mergers flounder at this stage due to a failure to appreciate properly the property considerations.

One practice may have plenty of equity while another may have very little, meaning an increase in borrowing in order to buy in. Existing borrowing terms may differ radically and, for example, one partnership may have punitive redemption penalties on a mortgage whereas the other may have very flexible and advantageous terms of borrowing.

Fitness for purpose and statutory compliance of the premises involved should be considered carefully to identify potentially hidden liabilities.

Where properties are leasehold, the terms of the leases need to be reviewed and fully understood, and it may be that the landlord's consent is required for any lease transfer to take place. Leases also may contain hidden liabilities, such as dilapidations claims or service charge liabilities.

Stamp Duty Land Tax (SDLT) implications of any property transfers need to be understood and managed appropriately.

If retiring partners are to retain an interest in the properties, a lease should be considered between the property owners and the merged partnership.

'Pre-nup'

When starting a merger, the first step from a legal point of view is the production of what we at VWV call a 'pre-nup' – an agreement that, while not binding the parties to go ahead and merge, binds them to share costs in agreed proportions during the preliminary phases. It will also contain confidentiality obligations to give both sides comfort that, while they each investigate each other's practices, any information disclosed remains strictly confidential and will not be spread 'round town'.

The pre-nup can also include any principles agreed between the partners on a non-binding basis, which functions as a set of 'heads of terms' for the deal. However, we caution practices against getting bogged down in detail at this stage and adding too much detail to what is a (mainly) non-binding agreement.

The outside world

Practice managers who are asked to manage a merger should be in no doubt that it is no minor task. We have limited ourselves to legal issues here, so this section does not go into the many practical tasks that will have to be carried out. One important practical issue, though, is to try to have a single person responsible for communications – it is unhelpful if mixed messages are passed round, and it is also important that one person is in charge of who knows what, and when patients, staff and suppliers are informed of what is happening.

Federations – a brief guide

Mike Gilbert and Scott McKenzie

Many of you will have read about – or even considered – practices coming together to form a federation, which amounts to practices uniting in a relationship having some interest, activity or purpose in common. It seems to us that the purpose is to share expertise, form buying consortia in order to reduce costs, adopt common approaches to day-to-day protocol, but in particular to combine to bid for Any Qualified Provider (AQP) work. In essence a federation formalises effective working between GPs, practices, healthcare professionals and other local providers such as community services and the private sector.

To get a federation off the ground, there need to be great leaders who have a vision, can articulate the vision, and share it with others. In this way, the others will identify what's in it for them; otherwise they are unlikely to engage at any level. Therefore, to get started, there needs to be an initial exploratory meeting, probably sponsored by specialist NHS consultants or accountants, to consider all the options available in the locality and determine what would and what wouldn't work for you. You will need to consider how locally you ensure that vital primary care infrastructure does not become threatened at a time when services are routinely being switched into primary and community settings with little or no funding. This initial meeting will start the process of ensuring that you have a strong local general practice that will be able to secure high-quality services.

At the end of the initial meeting you will all decide on whether you are to progress. Assuming you receive a positive response, you will then appoint a working party of, say, seven to ten people who will be responsible for developing the rules and protocol for what will become your company. This will include a decision as to whether the organisation will be for profit or otherwise. Those involved in working party meetings should always start with the desired end in mind and develop appropriate structures and governance to ensure that what is delivered meets required local outcomes.

The next full meeting should allow all interested practices to hear the conclusions of the working party, review any documents presented, and question the working party about any aspect of the company and plans for the future. Remember that the development of a GP federation should be viewed as an integral part of the Clinical Commissioning Group's (CCG) proactive approach to market management. When defined in this context the project does not constitute a potential conflict of interest. The role of the CCG is to facilitate discussion of potential options for cooperation and to enable practices to explore various opportunities. As such there is no reason why CCG board members cannot be involved.

Having completed the second meeting, practices should then be given time (say three weeks) to consider both all that has been said and the documentation, and to seek legal and accountancy advice on the best approach for them individually. At this stage practices need to decide on whether or not to sign up. To assist in the process, practices can also use this time to ask further questions of the working party. In addition, those who may be interested in becoming directors of the new company can put their names forward to seek election. Remember, this is an individual decision for practices, so you either accept the design principles and requirements of running a legal entity, or choose to remain outside of the process. At the end of this time period, practices will be asked to 'sign up' to the process and make nominations for board membership.

You are now in a position to finalise the board nominations and hold the election, which may or may not be dealt with at a further meeting. The Local Medical Committee (LMC) can be consulted to assist with the board election if necessary. Remember that those seeking election will need to have the necessary skills and be aware of the legal duties and responsibilities of becoming a director. It is not a position to be entered into lightly, but for the right people it can be a highly rewarding experience. For those seeking election a pen picture should be submitted to all practices as part of the election papers.

Having completed the election you now have a board in place, and you are now in a position to instruct lawyers to commence the process of registering the company and drafting the shareholders' agreement and articles of association. Remember that until this is done you cannot register for AQP or tender for any opportunities. The working party will initiate this process and at the same time guide the initial board meeting by setting the agenda to get them started.

The agenda for the initial board meeting will be quite extensive and can include as many topics as the members wish to raise. However, the following matters are essential:

- instructing lawyers and accountants
- developing the initial risk register
- appointing the leads for each area of risk identified
- appointing the leads to get the company registered with the Care Quality Commission (CQC)
- completing the registration so far as concerns information governance
- agreeing the board roles for all directors
- scheduling board meetings ahead.

It is possible that it will take more than one meeting to deal with the above issues, but their importance cannot be underestimated. It is all about setting and then managing expectations, but remember you will have very limited resources in the early stages, and even if the company grows quickly you will be unlikely to want to spend more than 5% of total turnover on administering the company and board. In the early days this figure is likely to lie between 10% and 15%, and the board will need to work hard to generate the income to reduce that percentage take-out for running costs.

Developing the initial risk register and appointing leads for each area of risk identified is an absolute 'must' in order to protect the company, the directors and the shareholders. This is about identifying how catastrophic an event could be if it happened and weighing up the likelihood of such an event occurring, right down the scale from certain to happen to rare. In this way you will be able to identify the risks that need your immediate attention to manage.

Appointing the leads to get the company registered with the CQC and completing the registration around information governance are essential because the CQC requires the company to be registered and to notify the sites it will work from, and you are required to be compliant with the information governance requirements of being an NHS provider. Failure to comply with either of these will eliminate the company from holding NHS contracts.

Having dealt with the essential issues, you are now in a position to develop a robust business plan to set you off on the right lines and make you think carefully about what you want to achieve and how. This should not be an extensive formal document but rather an action plan covering items you wish to work on both now and into the future. There are numerous items you could work on, but as a guide the following areas are recommended for consideration:

- 'scanning the horizon' for possible bids and tenders, as well as considering services you could develop
- getting the finances moving with some internal trading between practices, possibly with input from the CCG, e.g. education meetings
- with a view to reducing practice overheads, working to creating a buying consortia in such areas as medical supplies, insurances, utilities, mobile phones, stationery, consumables, etc. A federation has considerable buying power when purchasing on behalf of a number of practices
- carefully exploring any opportunity you may have to federate back-office support functions. While there may be significant opportunities in this area, it will need careful management. But remember it is an evolution and not a revolution
- setting up initial exploratory meetings with CCGs, the Foundation Trust, public health, local authority, community providers, community and voluntary sector, other local federations and other local stakeholders. This will enable you to understand how you can work locally with other providers and establish a relationship with your commissioners. At these

meetings you will be able to discuss new contracting options for prime, alliance and principal contracting.

In addition to the above business planning, you will need to agree the reporting lines for board meetings and how the information will be gathered and reported. Board meetings will include a number of standard items such as finance, audit, clinical governance and quality, corporate governance and risks. The board will also have expectations regarding those who deliver services to report activity, incidents, complaints, patient feedback and other issues, and will need to develop a standard format for such matters and consider how it will be collated for the board meetings. Included in reporting you should undertake a skills audit of all member practices, as well as a training needs analysis that should include the directors.

Much therefore needs to be done to set up a federation and get it working efficiently, but do not get downhearted by the process, but rather focus on the key driver, which is to allow general practice to respond to the challenges it currently faces. As such, rethinking the delivery model and developing new models of general practice will be key. Some of the thought processes you might adopt when considering federating or otherwise may be:

- sustainability – as there is a real risk that some practices will become unviable
- given that the NHS needs high-quality general practice to be successful and the current funding and income pressures are likely to grow and not go away, will you be able to encourage the membership to engage and work with you?
- how you protect and then build on the strength of general practice as the home of primary care – what services can you introduce as a result of federating?
- how you offer a long-term future to your current workforce through a workforce development plan for the short, medium and long term. The federation offers a long-term solution to avoid redundancy for both clinical and administrative teams, and you need to establish this quickly
- integrated services in the community
- how you plan to deliver long-term and sustainable change through a shift in mindset and work practices to deliver the new outcomes required, underpinned by high-quality training and education
- how you will focus upon improving outcomes
- how ultimately you will deliver your own business plan.

The decision is yours. You must consider whether you can afford not to be involved as it will be difficult for all but the largest practices to survive in isolation. The best you can hope for is a steady decline in income and an increase in workload.

FEDERATIONS – THE LAWYER'S PERSPECTIVE

Anthony Young

Introduction

The concept of practices collaborating is very much part of the primary care landscape these days. Federations mean different things to different people but the joining of forces to create a better outcome is nothing new. What is new is the sense that practices need to join in order not to miss out. We consider what a practice should consider before becoming a shareholder in a federation company.

How does being a shareholder in the company affect my practice?

Generally the shareholder will be the practice, and the shares will be partnership property. Typically the shares are registered in the name of one of the partners holding on trust for all of the partners. You should ensure your partnership deed and the articles of association of the company specify what happens if the nominated shareholder retires, or if there is a practice merger.

Practices must consider how they will exercise their rights as a shareholder. On the face of it the nominated shareholder has the right to exercise all the votes as he or she sees fit. However, it is important that the practice's partnership deed provides that the nominated shareholder must cast his or her votes with the authority/direction of the other partners. The same is true of dividends received, and any other benefits or obligations in the shareholders' agreement.

How can we sell our shares?

Generally there will be a prohibition on share transfers for an initial period, say three years. Practices need to ensure they understand this at the outset by checking the shareholders' agreement. Transfers from one nominated shareholder to another would be permitted.

A practice cannot simply 'retire' from the federation in the way that a partner in a practice can give notice, retire and be paid out his or her share capital.

A practice wishing to 'resign' as a shareholder will have to follow the share transfer procedure in the company's articles of association. This often creates an annual share transfer 'window'. A practice can give notice that it wishes to sell its shares in the window, following a prescribed valuation mechanism. This will often be based on the company's earnings, profit, balance sheet, etc.

A shareholder may seek to sell at any other time but typically will not receive the full potential value available by selling in a transfer window. A sale at any other time will be at a reduced value or as may otherwise be agreed between the company and the shareholder.

What liability do we have as shareholders?

A shareholder has no liability, generally, other than the obligation to pay the subscription monies for its shares. So if the company fails, the practice loses its investment but nothing more.

What do we pay for our shares and when do we subscribe?

The company will determine the number and type of shares subscribed for, usually based on practice size, and a price per share.

A practice will need to consider if it wants to join at the outset (i.e. when the company is formed) or join later. Clearly the founders hope to get as many members as possible at the outset, as the critical mass this will provide will help ensure the early success of the company. A shareholder who joins later is unlikely to get any better terms. The practice may even find itself left out if the company decides not to admit any further shareholders. A practice unsure whether to join at the outset could negotiate an option to acquire shares at the initial share price, but this is only likely to be granted for a limited duration, e.g. six months.

The company will be keen to join shareholders in as early as possible, underlining the 'better together' message.

Will our practice be prevented from competing with the company?

A shareholder is not automatically prevented from competing with a company in which it is a shareholder. Usually, though, the company will require its shareholders not to compete with it while they are shareholders and for a specified period of time (typically between one and two years) after ceasing to be a shareholder.

This gives practices an important decision to make: are we better off alone with the freedom to compete with the company or are we better off as part of the company although potentially subject to restrictions on what services we can carry out? Considering the company's business plan may help answer this question.

A partnership with a potential competing interest should negotiate specific exemptions from the restrictive covenant, but any exemptions will need to be precisely worded and very clear. This negotiation has to happen before the practice joins up of course – afterwards it will be too late.

If one of the practice's partners is a director of the company it would be more difficult for that practice to seek release from the restrictive covenants. A director must act in the best interest of the company (rather than in his or her practice's interests). Moreover he or she would not be able to use any confidential information obtained about the company to the practice's advantage when competing for services against the company or when bidding for contracts awarded by the company.

Who runs the company and what influence do we have over the board, and can we hold the directors to account?

The company will be run by its board of directors. The directors will usually have been appointed on the incorporation of the company and, typically, all the directors will resign at the first annual general meeting. Those initial directors and any other directors who wish to put themselves forward will then seek re-election at the first annual general meeting. This is usually for a set period of office, e.g. three years. It is common for a proportion of the directors (usually one-third) to retire automatically at each subsequent annual general meeting. To continue in office they must be re-elected by the members. This is a critical means of holding the directors to account and, effectively, to prevent them from continuing in office.

In addition, a majority of shareholders may remove a director from office at any point using the procedure set out in the Companies Act 2006. The board would then nominate a replacement whose appointment would be ratified by the shareholders (as he or she would retire automatically at the next general meeting following his or her appointment).

How is our relationship affected if we are both a shareholder and supplier to the company?

A shareholder in a federation will typically earn income from 1) any dividends declared from time to time and 2) services it provides to the company. The basis on which a shareholder contracts with the company should be set out in a service contract that clearly defines roles, responsibilities, basis for payments, etc.

A shareholder would not be liable to forfeit its shares if there is a dispute over the contract. Damages or other remedies may be due if there is a breach of the contract, but it would be highly unusual for this to extend to the shares.

It is essential that any arrangements by which member practices will provide services to/for the federation are clearly documented. This should be done at the outset as, once in place, arrangements can be hard to change, and may even have become a legally enforceable contractual position. Contracting on 'standard NHS terms' is a misnomer. The shareholders should ensure that – and if need be challenge the company to ensure – any contracts have been properly drafted and the company has taken legal advice on the rights and obligations under the contract, because this has an impact on all the shareholders. Failing to do so may save costs in the short term but is certainly not best practice, and is likely to store up trouble for the future.

Conclusion

Federations are high on the agenda. A strong business case and well-drafted business plan will help create a successful company that will bring value to its shareholders. In considering how and when to join this, a practice must ensure:

- its own partnership deed is up to date and deals with the practicalities of being a shareholder in the company
- that it understands clearly what it will pay for its shares and how it (and any other shareholder) can exit the company. The practice should ask for an option to subscribe for shares if it is not ready to become a shareholder at the outset
- it negotiates clear exemptions to any non-compete restrictions and considers carefully whether one of its partners should be a director of the company in these circumstances
- that the contracting arrangements between the company and its members for services are properly documented and the rights and obligations of each party are clearly defined.

Federations – identifying and managing conflicts of interest

Scott McKenzie

Concerns about the identification and then management of conflict of interest can cause barriers to progress in the emergence of federations. What exactly is a conflict of interest? Here are two definitions that explain what it is, with insight into how to manage actual and perceived conflicts:

- a conflict of interest is a set of conditions in which professional judgement concerning a primary interest (such as patients' welfare) tends to be unduly influenced by a secondary interest (such as financial gain)[1]
- a conflict of interest is a situation in which one's ability to exercise judgement in one role is impaired by one's obligation in another.[2]

When might a conflict of interest arise? Put simply, when you are involved in decision making where any of the following apply and you have a:

- direct financial interest
- indirect financial interest
- personal interest
- conflict of loyalties
- conflict of professional duties.

This doesn't mean everything grinds to a halt though. The goal of a strong policy to manage conflict of interest should be to allow the business of the organisation to safely proceed.

For Clinical Commissioning Groups (CCGs), they will all have a policy embedded within the constitution, which should ensure a register of members' interests is available for inspection at all times. Additionally, the accountable officer should ensure that every interest is declared and there are arrangements to manage any conflicts, with all decisions and reasons for decisions documented and available for scrutiny.

Conflicted individuals should be excluded from relevant parts of meetings; however, if this were to leave insufficient un-conflicted individuals the CCG must have a policy for this, which should provide for a different committee/sub-committee or *ad hoc* group being able to take decisions. For example, this could include members from another CCG or Health and Wellbeing Board. If that isn't enough the governing body can seek additional scrutiny of decisions through its own audit committee or from external individuals. Therefore there really is no situation that cannot be safely managed.

The aim of a process to manage conflict of interest is not to prevent people from having any private interests, but rather to protect the integrity of the CCG, its members and administrative decisions generally. The CCG should want to promote a culture where conflict of interest is properly identified, managed and resolved in an appropriate, transparent and timely way. Unfortunately, though, what we are finding is the conflict of interest issue being used as a weapon to stifle or prevent legitimate debate.

The key point to make is that conflict of interest applies where people are involved in making commissioning decisions that they as providers would benefit from – this simply cannot happen. Included within that is the development of service specifications, where providers should have no input, as clearly they gain significant advantage over other providers not included in the development and that is likely to have serious repercussions.

Both scenarios need managing, and both can safely be managed through a sensible policy and a complete understanding of how to manage conflict of interest. The fact many GPs and practice managers will be involved in Provider Organisations and CCG meetings is in itself not a conflict; only where they are involved in decision making does the potential for conflict of interest arise.

A sense of proportionality is required above all else.

REFERENCES
1. Thompson DF. Understanding financial conflicts of interest. *New England Journal of Medicine* 1993; **329(8):** 573–576.
2. Roll Back Malaria Partnership. *Conflict of Interest Policy and Procedure*. Geneva: WHO, 2009, www.rbm.who.int/docs/constituencies/RBMcoiPolicy.pdf [accessed 18 February 2015].

FEDERATIONS – DIVISION OF RESPONSIBILITIES WITHIN THE BOARD

Scott McKenzie

Sharing the workload equally amongst the directors is not going to be as simple and straightforward as it sounds. It is however a crucial process that needs to be determined at the outset, otherwise you risk one or two people having a significant workload and others with little to do. The risk then would be that there is only one voice leading the whole process, which is a recipe for disaster.

The early key roles are likely to be:

Chief executive
This individual needs to drive the business forward, sharing the vision and values of the organisation and really selling your company to all stakeholders.

Medical directors
Individuals with strong clinical knowledge and an innovative approach are a must for the type of services you will be delivering.

Contracts and contract monitoring
Someone who will work to negotiate and secure business for the company is required.

Communications and engagement
The key to early success is being able to demonstrate the engagement of the membership, and the ability to act as one corporate body. It is not an easy task to achieve and not a role to underestimate.

Corporate governance

One of the directors will need to pay close attention to the articles of association and shareholders' agreement, and, at the same time, start to get a grasp of basic company law. Clearly legal support for this role is recommended; however, it does need to sit within the company.

Finance

An individual to oversee the income and expenditure, and early support from a specialist medical accountant, may be advantageous to guide you in the early stages.

Each role will find workload ebbs and flows depending on what the company is doing; however, based on experience it is safe to assume that planning for three or four sessions a month is not unreasonable.

These sessions will of course need to be in normal working hours, as that's when your other stakeholders will be available to work with you.

For those becoming directors, it is therefore really a career decision they are making as this is not something you can simply fit in now and again when you have a bit of time, particularly when the company starts to grow and more time is required in your role as a director. To truly take ownership over your roles and to be successful, you have to allocate the right resource at the outset.

NEW GP PREMISES COSTS DIRECTIONS

Mike Gilbert

The valuation of your surgery premises could be significantly affected by the Premises Costs Directions 2013, which have replaced the 2004 Directions. While the Directions are particularly detailed, the following is a summary of the most important changes of which GPs should now be aware.

1. Private income

Previously, GPs needed to declare private income arising from work performed in the practice premises, typically commercial contracts and work done for private patients. Where such income exceeded 10% of the total income, the rent reimbursement was adjusted downwards accordingly. However, such a declaration is now no longer necessary. As a sting in the tail, the Department of Health has also stated that practices found to be carrying out particularly high levels of private work in their practice premises will still find that their rent reimbursement will be reduced.

2. Leased premises – rent review

GPs will now need to appoint a specialist surveyor to assist them in negotiating a rent with the landlord or the landlord's surveyor. This is because practices who lease their premises will need to negotiate a new rent with their landlord when a rent review is due, and duly record the outcome before applying for notional rent. Once your own specialist surveyor has provisionally agreed a rent, they will then be able to discuss notional rent with the District Valuer.

3. Mortgages

So far as concerns borrowings for surgery premises, a major problem often arises from the astronomical penalties incurred when GPs attempt to repay their long-term mortgages with high fixed-interest rates and replace them with cheaper borrowing arrangements. The new Directions enable NHS England to cover the penalty costs, but of course this is subject to NHS England's own budgetary targets and the savings arising in respect of recurring premises reimbursements.

4. Approval for sale and leaseback, and developments

From now on approval must be obtained from NHS England before practices undertake a sale and leaseback arrangement on the surgery premises.
Similarly, development work must be approved by NHS England prior to
commencement, otherwise financial assistance will definitely not be granted.

5. Improvement grants

Premises improvement grants are now available for the following works:

a   Improvements for infection control purposes
b   Water meter installations
c   Connections to emergency generators
d   Electronic storage facilities.

The following works are not included in the scheme:

a   General wear and tear
b   Solar panels and replacement windows, or indeed any other improve-
    ments to reduce the environmental impact of premises.

6. Car parking

GPs will now need to check whether tandem spaces are included in their
notional rent valuation. This is necessary because it appears that tandem
spaces, which are often adopted in busy central locations, will no longer be
approved for reimbursement. Although the wording is not absolutely clear, it
appears that the number of reimbursable car parking spaces must be approved
by NHS England and access to and egress from each space must be possible
without the need to move other cars. The rules certainly seem stricter than
hitherto.

7. Notional rent valuations based on alternative use

Some surgeries are currently valued on what is known as an alternative use
basis. Typically, these surgeries are located in very high-value areas. However,
the ability to value a surgery on this basis has been removed, which means that
practices who have thus far been valued on this basis will probably experience
a significant reduction in their notional rent reimbursement.

***

It seems to be that a day does not pass without some change arising for medical practices. In this instance, further work needs to be done and practices
may well find it beneficial to appoint a specialist to help them, such as GP
Surveyors.

GP PROPERTY OWNERSHIP

Ben Willis

GP practices are unusual! GP premises costs are reimbursed by the NHS, by way of a notional rent where the property is freehold, or by way of rent reimbursement where the property is leasehold.

Entitlement to this reimbursement derives from the core NHS GP contract, which is ongoing with no fixed term. While the contract continues, the reimbursement is effectively government-backed income and so this makes GPs an attractive proposition to banks and property investors, willing to rely on the GP 'covenant' for lending or property investment purposes.

This, along with the technical issues that arise around partnership property, has meant that GP premises ownership has become something of a specialist area for professional advisers and banks.

Partnership property

The majority of GP practice premises are owned by partners as partnership property.

Whether or not property is partnership property is a question of fact. It may be shown in the accounts as partnership property or it may be identified in the partnership agreement as partnership property. Neither is definitive but the assumption for the purposes of this chapter is that property is partnership property.

Where partnership property is jointly owned by more than one partner, it is automatically held on a 'trust for land'.

The title to the property can be registered in the names of no more than four partners (and at least two), who will hold the property as trustees. The partners named on the title hold on trust for all the property owners in accordance with their beneficial interests in the property from time to time.

The shares in which the property is held are usually shown in the partnership accounts and sometimes are expressly set out in the partnership agreement. However, we don't recommend this, due to the administrative burden of documenting any changes in the partnership shares.

The terms on which property is held by the partnership and any provisions relating to valuation and what happens on retirement should be expressly set out, either in the partnership agreement or in a separate property trust deed.

Non-property-owning partners

The existence of non-property-owning partners can sometimes raise difficult issues and, although it is of course a decision for each partnership, it can make life considerably easier for all involved if all partners in the practice have the same status when it comes to property ownership. It is not possible to bind incoming partners to existing partnership arrangements, unless they agree to them, and, with recruitment of partners getting more difficult, it is not always possible to achieve the preferred outcome.

Non-property-owning partners can have specific concerns such as:

PARTNERSHIP BORROWING

Non-property owners will wish to consider an express exclusion from any property loans, on the basis that they do not wish to share joint and several liability for a loan in respect of a property in which they have no interest. Banks tend to prefer loans to the whole partnership jointly (although individual loans are not uncommon) and the difficulty here is that all partners are jointly and severally liable for partnership liabilities, whatever the arrangements between the partners.

While the non-property owners (should) benefit from an indemnity from the property owners in the partnership agreement, they may also try to agree that they do not sign the loan agreement and request a letter from the bank confirming that the bank will not hold the non-property-owning partners responsible for the partnership loan. This is often overlooked.

MAINTENANCE AND REPAIRS

Property-owning partners will wish to ensure that they benefit from all notional rent, to (hopefully) cover the property liabilities. An area of frequent debate is whether the maintenance and repair of the property should be the responsibility of the property owners or of the whole partnership.

Some will argue that the partners who get the notional rent should cover the property maintenance and repair costs, building up a sinking fund from the notional rent received. Some will say that the partnership gets the benefit of the use of the premises and so should cover all the costs of maintenance and repair.

This is a matter for agreement within each partnership.

IS A LEASE NEEDED?

No lease is required where there are non-property-owning partners and the property can still be held as partnership property, even if owned by some but not all of the partners. Non-property owners will occupy either under an express licence in the partnership agreement or under an implied licence to occupy.

Partners retaining a property share post-retirement

As we have seen, GP premises are seen as a good 'investment' and it is often the case that, on retirement, partners want to hold on to their share in the property and continue to benefit from a share in the income. Again, although not uncommon, it does throw up a number of potentially awkward issues (as well as further fertile ground for dispute).

The good advice is that the partnership deed should expressly reflect the intention of the partners (whatever is agreed), rather than leave it for discussion when someone retires. Retiring partners should also take tax advice as Capital Gains Tax (CGT) could be an issue for them.

IS A LEASE NEEDED?

Where retiring partners retain a share in the surgery premises, it is likely that a separate 'property-owning partnership' is automatically created between the retired partner and the continuing partners, which is distinct from the continuing medical partnership.

Arguably, a periodic tenancy is created at that point between the property owners on the one hand and the medical partnership on the other, as tenant. If it is left undocumented, then there will be uncertainty over the terms of that tenancy and the medical partners may well acquire rights of security of tenure against the property owners. The retired partner is no longer entitled to notional rent, but will want to be paid a 'real' rent of equivalent value.

A written lease should certainly be considered, to expressly set out the terms of the tenancy, e.g. as to rent and rent review (usually linked to NHS reimbursement), repair and service charge, permitted use (non-NHS?), contractual term, security of tenure, etc.

The downside is the costs involved and the need to pay Stamp Duty Land Tax (SDLT) on the rent as well as the requirement for NHS England consent to the lease terms and the change in status from notional rent to rent reimbursement.

The upside of a written lease is certainty as to responsibility for the property costs for both parties, security of occupation for the medical practice and ensuring that the retired partner has an enforceable right to receive the rent due.

A NEW PROPERTY DEED?

Once a partner has retired, it does not 'work' to include property provisions in the partnership deed, as the retired partner will not still be a party to it. If a separate property deed wasn't set up at the outset, then it is good advice to put one in place at this point, to document the ownership relationship going forwards. This would cover, for example, what happens should an owner subsequently wish to sell and how that share would be valued.

It is extremely important that the registered title to the property is kept up to date when partners leave or join. Outgoing partners will be concerned as to the potential for continuing liability and the continuing partners will be keen to manage their own liabilities as well as retaining control in dealing with the property and the title.

Leases

Leases to partnerships will be held by some or all of the partners on behalf of the partnership. Only the first four of the partners named on a lease can be registered at the Land Registry. They will hold the lease on trust for the partnership as tenant. It is common therefore for some but not all partners to be named on a lease.

The partners who sign the lease will remain liable under the terms of the lease for the full length of the term unless the lease is expressly transferred to new partners. In most commercial leases, on a transfer, the outgoing partners can be required to guarantee the obligations of the incoming tenant partners. Most GP leases include provisions to ensure outgoing partners are released from continuing liability, subject to there being a minimum number of partners on the lease from time to time, which enables retiring partners to retire free of any liability.

Where the minimum number is reached (between two and four usually) then a retiring partner would still expect to be released from continuing liability if replaced as tenant by a continuing partner in the practice.

Generally, where a lease is held for a partnership, all partners are liable for the lease obligations while they are partners. However, if they are not named on the lease, then they are released on retirement without the need for further documentation.

Note that while NHS England is responsible for reimbursing rent, there is no obligation to step in and take over a lease if the partnership fails or the retiring partners cannot find any continuing partners to take the lease over. If partners are left holding the lease with no successors willing to take over, they remain liable to continue to pay rent and other outgoings, and to comply with all the other tenant's covenants under the lease, whether or not rent reimbursement from NHS England continues.

NHS England approval is required for the commercial terms of any new lease, and very often the form of lease itself will be subject to approval.

Key lease terms

There is a whole suite of restrictions and obligations in a lease setting out what the tenant can and cannot do. Leases tend to follow a similar format but there is no standard form of lease and terms can vary considerably, making it important to negotiate and understand lease terms fully.

The key lease terms to be aware of are as follows (overleaf):

USE

Most landlords will want to see use restricted to NHS primary care purposes, as this drives entitlement to rent reimbursement from NHS England and therefore enhances the value of the landlord's investment. Whether or not they currently provide non-NHS services, with the current rapid pace of change GP tenants would want to have flexibility to provide wider services without having to ask for specific consent, which may or may not fall outside NHS use.

ALTERATIONS

There will be restrictions on alterations and most will require consent from the landlord. Be aware that alterations carried out without NHS England approval may not entitle the tenant to increased rent reimbursement to reflect the value of the improvements.

ASSIGNMENTS AND SUBLETTINGS

Landlord's consent will generally be required for any lease transfer or for the creation of sublettings and licences. See comments above over flexibility on assignment to new partners. If there is a likelihood of formal subletting (e.g. a pharmacy) or sharing occupation with third parties (NHS trusts, district nurses, etc.), landlord's consent should be requested.

SECURITY OF TENURE

Both landlords and tenants should be aware of the provisions of the Landlord and Tenant Act 1954, which gives to business tenants rights of 'security of tenure' and the right to apply for a new lease when the existing lease comes to an end. The provisions relating to partnerships are complex, and specialist advice should be sought.

LANDLORD'S CONSENT

Where landlord's consent is required, the landlord is not usually obliged to give it, except where reasonable to do so, and will usually want to document that consent by way of a formal licence. There will be cost implications to this.

RENT AND RENT REVIEW

Tenant GPs will wish to link the rent they pay under the lease to the rent that is reimbursed by the NHS, both from the outset and on rent review. Until recently, it was possible to link the rent payable under the lease on review to the level of reimbursement assessed by the District Valuer and approved by the Commissioner. Due to recent changes in the regulations that govern notional rent and rent reimbursement (the NHS Property Directions 2013) this can be harder to do, and a full rent review will need to be negotiated and agreed with the landlord before an application to NHS England for reimbursement can be made. This means that there is a risk of a shortfall between the level of rent payable to the landlord and the amount of reimbursement that can be claimed from NHS England. There are ways to mitigate this risk.

REPAIR

Usually, a GP tenant will have an internal repairing obligation, with the landlord accepting responsibility for the structure and external parts of the building. This reflects the way in which rent reimbursement is calculated, but it is not always the case. There can be a significant dilapidations liability at the end of a lease and so careful consideration should be given to these provisions.

PROPERTY TAXES

Leases trigger a liability to pay SDLT, which can be significant, and advice should be taken on the amounts due. VAT is also often an issue with commercial leases, because GPs have very limited scope to recover VAT. NHS England will not always reimburse VAT payable on rent and so it is an area that requires consideration and advice.

In summary, leases are complex commercial documents, and specialist advice should be taken by both landlords and tenants if a lease is contemplated.

The National Health Service (General Medical Services – Premises Costs) Directions 2013 – the Directions

GPs are entitled to property costs under their General Medical Services (GMS)/ Personal Medical Services (PMS) contract and the rules governing this are set out in the Directions. The most recent Directions, brought into effect in 2013, updated the previous Directions, which have been in place since 2004. A number of changes were made. These new Directions are themselves under review and an updated version is expected during 2015.

In the majority of cases, the District Valuer will be instructed by NHS England to assess the value of premises so that a notional rent or rent reimbursement can be settled. On new schemes there is flexibility on the part of NHS England to accept the recommendations of the District Valuer and, in many cases, affordability will drive how much can actually be paid and it is not always the case that the full amount of a rent agreed and/or VAT will be payable.

Notional rent is reviewed every three years and guidance as to the basis upon which the valuation will be carried out is set out in the Directions. This is a particularly specialist area and it is strongly recommended that proper professional valuation advice from an experienced surveyor is taken when dealing with notional rent and rent review.

There are various flexibilities under the Directions for other costs and awards to be made, e.g. development grants, SDLT, fees and (sometimes) contributions to redemption penalties.

There is also scope for abatements to be made in the event that a GP practice in receipt of a notional rent or rent reimbursement receives contributions to property costs from a third party. It is surprisingly common for third parties to occupy parts of surgeries and contribute in some way to premises costs. Care should be taken not to trigger an abatement.

NHS consent will also be required if a GP practice wants to sell its freehold premises and lease it back.

GP surgery developments

The development of GP surgeries is something of a niche specialist area and worthy of a much more detailed consideration than there is room for here. Because of the entitlement of GPs to notional rent from the NHS, banks are prepared to lend to GP practices 100% of development finance on favourable terms, assuming a project is otherwise financially viable.

Likewise, developers/investors are keen to sign GPs up on long (21–25 years) NHS-backed leases and carry out the development for them. These schemes create valuable investments and have led to the development of a niche property investment market of considerable value.

A property development is often the most high-value project a GP will be involved in during his or her career and the majority of GPs will be doing it for the first time. The potential pitfalls are many and varied, and the importance of an experienced professional team to provide guidance throughout and help deliver the project cannot be over-emphasised.

There are various different ways in which surgery premises are procured and the main ones are as follows:

DIY

The GP practice borrows money from a bank, buys land, gets planning permission, instructs a building contractor and carries out the development itself. This may well be done with the GP partnership as owner or by way of setting up a separate company, which owns the property, carries out the development and then lets the premises back to the GP partnership by way of a lease.

There are pros and cons in both structures, and the right one for each scheme will depend on the culture of the practice, the number of partners (and sometimes the number of practices) taking part, and plans for the future of the practice and the property. Sometimes the structure is driven by the preferences of the chosen professional advisers but each practice should be given the opportunity to weigh up which structure is right for them and their circumstances.

DIY involves the GPs taking the risk of all 'upfront' costs, such as planning, design and site acquisition, and the 'development risk' (something going 'wrong' during the development phase) but gives the practice the return of any capital growth over time, as well as the flexibility that comes with being owner.

THIRD-PARTY DEVELOPMENT

Third-party development (3PD) involves the acquisition and development of the surgery by an independent developer/investor. The GPs will be required to sign an agreement for lease before the development commences and, once the development has completed, will sign a lease, typically of 20–25 years, which is backed by rent reimbursement from the NHS. This limits the upfront costs and exposure of the medical partnership to any development risk, but does not give any interest in the capital value of the property and is subject to the ongoing liabilities and the restrictions of a lease.

In these transactions, the terms of the lease are particularly important and should be fully understood by the GP partners. The lease terms should be robustly negotiated at the heads of terms and lease drafting stages. Of equal importance is to the comprehensive and detailed agreement of the scope and quality of the building design to ensure the best building possible.

LOCAL IMPROVEMENT FINANCE TRUST

A number of surgeries have been developed to the Local Improvement Finance Trust (LIFT) scheme, which is a scheme not dissimilar to private finance initiative (PFI). Development by LIFT companies remains an option.

Since the NHS reforms in 2013, there has been a large degree of uncertainty as to the future direction the NHS will take for the funding and procurement of new surgery buildings. It has proven to be very difficult to achieve NHS sign-off for new developments since 2013. However, with the publication of the NHS five-year plan and recent announcements that more funding will be made available for GP practices and premises, it is hoped that surgery developments will again be able to proceed. With a large number of practice premises no longer 'fit for purpose' and overcrowded, and a desire to see more services being provided by GPs in a local setting, it is difficult to see how the NHS vision can be delivered without significant investment in the primary care infrastructure.

NHS PROPERTY SERVICES LIMITED

The creation of NHS Property Services Limited (Propco – a limited company owned by the Secretary of State), which has taken over the ownership of most existing NHS property, has added further uncertainty.

Numerous GP practices occupy health centres owned by Propco, which is now extremely reluctant to sell operational buildings. Propco will presumably wish to carry out future redevelopment of NHS-owned buildings and will wish existing occupants of health centres to sign leases to document their occupation, whether there is a development or not. Whereas Propco prefers a 'standard' approach to this, each party will have its own practice issues and building-specific issues that will need to be dealt with in each lease negotiation. It is important to consider carefully the future liabilities of the practice, particularly for rent, service charge and repair, before entering into any formal lease arrangements.

Third-party occupants

Where a practice wishes to share the premises with third-party occupants, such as health trusts, community healthcare services or other healthcare operators, it is important the occupation is properly documented.

Informal occupations may be documented by way of a licence, but more permanent occupations that grant exclusive possession and where a rent is payable should be documented by way of a lease and with the benefit of proper professional advice. It is important to avoid the occupant inadvertently gaining rights of security of tenure (see above) and also that any rental or other income for the property does not impact on the notional rent or rent reimbursement received by the practice.

Tax

Tax on partnership property transactions is very often a major factor in the decision-making process. While the tax 'tail' should not be allowed to wag the transaction 'dog', tax planning for any property transaction and a full consideration of CGT, VAT and SDLT liabilities and possible capital allowances (where appropriate) can save significant sums of money and should certainly be taken into account when considering which is the appropriate structure for a development.

LOAN FOR SURGERY PROPERTY

Ian Crompton

The biggest debt taken on by a GP partnership is usually the one relating to the surgery property.

As outlined in the 'Loan Affordability' Topic (see p. 97), the main consideration for a bank will be ensuring that the business/practice has enough free income to service the loan repayment.

Many funding providers consider GP surgery loans as a safe sector, with credit policies that reflect a low rate of loss. Some banks have a credit policy that allows for funding up to 100% of the value of a property, or up to 105% for new developments. Simply, if the loan repayments are covered by rent reimbursement from the NHS, the lending process should be straightforward. However, in many recent cases, the building may have space used for non-General Medical Services (GMS)/Personal Medical Services (PMS) services that are not covered by 'guaranteed' NHS payments.

Even when the property is mainly GMS/PMS the rent reimbursement offered is likely to be insufficient to cover loan repayments at 100% 'loan to value'. This is because the rent reimbursement is calculated in a way that assumes an interest rate below that which is currently available on the market.

It should also be recognised that rent reimbursement does not cover capital repayments, so, in addition to making up any shortfall in respect of interest, doctors will also need to fund the capital repayments. Banks will often allow 'interest only' to be paid for a number of years with the expectation that rent reimbursements will increase at the next review, but this cannot be guaranteed and, if unavailable, the partners will need to find the extra commitment.

Another consideration is that of potential base rate movements. Rent reimbursement currently agreed will be while the base rate is 0.5%, but many observers believe the rate could rise at some stage, albeit at a slow pace. This would result in an increase on the interest rate on the loan, creating a potential gap between what the NHS pays and the loan repayment – a 1% rise would add approximately £416 per month to the cost of a £500,000 loan, and should be taken into consideration before taking the decision to invest.

The issue of valuation must also be considered. There is a value known as a trading concern, which is when it is a fully functioning GP surgery with rent being paid. Then there is the 'closed' or 'alternative use' value, which is looking at the value assuming the property is no longer a GP surgery with a tenant in place.

The difference in the two valuations will vary on many factors. Recent examples involve small practices where the 'alternative use' was to convert back to a residential home. The first in East Yorkshire was worth far less than the business valuation and the second in the Home Counties was worth far more. Clearly if the 'alternative use' value is close to or higher than the current trading value there is less risk overall. The bank likes to know the detail and this should be an important consideration for any partners looking to invest.

Tenants and leases will be a further concern. If NHS rent reimbursement is not enough to cover the loan repayments on its own, it needs to be clear where the shortfall will be made up. It is increasingly common for surgeries to have tenants such as a pharmacy, district nurse or dental practice. Ideally the tenant's monthly rental contributions in addition to the rent reimbursement will cover the loan repayment. However, the term of lease is also to be reviewed – a short lease of five years does not support a loan as much as one for 20 years. The 'credit rating' of the tenant should also be considered as one who is unreliable or may not survive should be avoided.

For GPs that have weighed this up and made the decision to invest in their premises, there is funding available from banks, and there always has been. Loans up to 100% of value will be considered, but there are many factors to take into account, mainly the ability to meet the loan repayments. If there is going to be a shortfall from the rent reimbursement, it is up to partners to be willing to use their profits to cover this gap.

It is likely that the days when surgery loans were simply covered by NHS rent reimbursement are long gone. The challenges around affordability are as much for the partners as for the bank, as investing in premises is a long-term commitment and needs to be thought through. In addition to speaking to a bank that understands GPs, it is recommended that you also speak to specialist accountants and law firm as tax, retirement planning and partnership agreements should also be taken into account.

LOAN AFFORDABILITY

Ian Crompton

It is common for people discussing finance to talk about 'loan to value' or LTV. This is normally a simple percentage figure of the value of the loan being sought over the value of the asset being purchased and provided as security. A typical example would be with domestic mortgages when a loan of £300,000 against a property costing £400,000 would be talked of as 75% loan to value.

Banks or other financial providers will also talk in terms of LTV but the decision to lend is not a simple matter of the lower the LTV, the more likely the lending will be agreed. It is one factor, but a more important consideration for a bank is the ability of the person or business to repay or 'service' the debt. Lending at say 50% is not going to work if the borrower cannot afford the loan repayments.

In the simple form of a personal mortgage a lender will look at the application's regular income, deduct all expenses such as living costs, car, insurance, etc. and then work out how much is available for loan repayments. A calculation sometimes used to show how affordable the loan is 'Debt Service Cover' (DSC). This is the amount of 'free' income divided by the loan repayment, e.g. surplus income of £500 per month against a loan repayment of £300 gives a debt service of 166%. The higher the DSC, the more affordable the loan.

This can be relatively easy to work out for a full-time employee with a regular salary and regular expenses but it is more difficult for a business. For businesses banks will normally ask to see three years of accounts and try to establish what an expected net profit will be, i.e. after all drawings and other costs and expenses. They may also ask for projections or forecasts to help assess the likely situation. As with a person applying for a mortgage the lender will ideally want to see regular reliable income.

On the face of it a 100% debt service cover may seem to be enough but a lender will normally expect a 'buffer' to allow for unexpected expenses or a fall in income. As an example a bank may look for, say, 125% DSC to ensure there is ample margin for unforeseen circumstances. In some sectors where income is less certain higher DSCs may be expected.

Another consideration is that of potential base rate movements. At the present time the base rate is 0.5%, but many observers believe the rate could rise at some stage, albeit at a slow pace. This would result in an increase on the interest rate on the loan, creating a potential gap between what is affordable when taking out the loan and the loan repayment at the higher rate. As an example of the possible impact a 1% rise would add approximately £416 per month to the cost of a £500,000 loan. For this reason banks will often 'stress-test' at a nominal base rate of, say, 4%, i.e. they work out if repayments would be affordable if base rate increased to 4%. It should be stressed that this 'stress-tested' calculation does not mean repayments will increase; that will depend on any base rate changes or the loan agreement. It is simply a calculation to ensure the loan could still be afforded if rates do rise.

LENDING AND SECURITY

Ian Crompton

When lending money a bank may ask for security. Banks do not normally lend to security; they lend to the proposition and take security to support the lending should anything go wrong. The primary consideration is the ability of the person, business or practice to service the loan, i.e. repay the loan.

Lenders may talk about 'tangible' security being the best security; this is distinct from 'intangible' security, which may not be considered as valuable as security for a loan. Tangible security normally refers to something that a person can 'touch and see' such as property. Tangible security can be valued and sold if necessary, and provided the bank gets the property 'legally charged' or 'mortgaged' properly it can (subject to various conditions) 'enter into possession' and control the sale. Tangible security values tend to be more measurable and stable, and this, coupled with the ability to take a legal charge, makes it good security.

Intangible security is something less certain. An example from the dental profession or pharmacy is 'goodwill'. This is the value attached to a business but it cannot be 'touched or seen', and while it undoubtedly has a value it is not generally reckoned to be as good as security as, say, property because it is difficult to tie down. Dental goodwill, for example, may largely attach to the dentist him or herself, i.e. the patients will follow the dentist if he or she moves, and this makes it difficult to use as security.

In a similar vein, lenders may refer to 'lending values'. These will be different for different banks (albeit similar) and are simple internal benchmarks set from experience giving a perceived safe level to which an item of security may be relied upon. An example may be for an owner-occupied property having a lending value of, say, 70%. What this means is that from experience property values may fluctuate by up to 30%, or in other words: a property valued today at £100k may only be worth £70k when the security is needed. It is important to remember here that security is usually only needed in times of financial difficulty and, as such, associated security values are likely to be lower than in 'boom' times.

Looking more specifically at property the issue of the valuation must also be considered. There is a value known as a trading concern, which is when it is a fully functioning GP surgery with rent being paid, and then there is the 'closed' or 'alternative use' value, which is looking at the value assuming the property is no longer a GP surgery with a tenant in place.

The difference in the two valuations will vary on many factors. Recent examples involve small practices where the 'alternative use' was to convert back to a residential home. The first in East Yorkshire was worth far less than the business valuation and the second in the Home Counties was worth far more. Clearly if the 'alternative use' value is close to or higher than the current trading value there is less risk overall. The bank likes to know the detail and this should be an important consideration for any partners looking to invest.

Tenants and leases will be a further concern. If NHS rent reimbursement is not enough to cover the loan repayments on its own, it needs to be clear where the shortfall is to be made up. It is increasingly common for surgeries to have tenants such as a pharmacy, district nurse or dental practice. Ideally the tenant's monthly rental contributions in addition to the rent reimbursement will cover the loan repayment. However, the term of lease is also to be reviewed – a short lease of five years does not support a loan as much as one for 20 years. The 'credit rating' of the tenant should also be considered as one who is unreliable or may not survive should be avoided.

It is usual for a bank to want the security properly in place and finalised before it will advance any money. In some cases 'perfecting' the security can take a significant length of time and it is recommended you plan early and allow sufficient time for all formalities to be completed. Property security can take a number of weeks to complete.

A final word on security: although a bank when lending looks at the ability of the borrower to repay first and the security second, if things go wrong the security can be used. A standard warning on mortgage documentation is 'your home may be repossessed if you do not keep up repayments' and similar applies to any security: if you default it can be called upon and you may lose possession. **It is recommended that you seek independent legal advice when providing security and are fully aware of the potential repercussions**.

Topic 30

OVERDRAFTS

Ian Crompton

Overdraft facilities are intended to be a facility to cover short-term cash short-falls on a bank current account; they should not normally be used to cover the cost of larger fixed assets such as equipment or property unless it is clear that cash due will clear borrowing in the near future (say six months), which should be financed by a loan. The general rule is that current accounts should 'swing' into credit regularly, e.g. be overdrawn for a few days/weeks and then back into credit before perhaps overdrawing again.

On a financial technical point: overdrafts are repayable on demand. This means a bank can ask for them to be cleared at any time (subject to the over-draft agreement) whereas a loan is committed for a longer term. In the financial accounts for the practice you will normally see 'current liabilities' and 'long-term liabilities'. Current liabilities are those payable in less than one year and long-term liabilities those payable over more than one year. A measure of the financial 'health' of a business is for monies you are due in the short term or 'current assets', e.g. cash, stock and debtors, to be worth more than current liabilities, e.g. creditors, tax and overdraft. The difference is referred to as 'Net Current Assets' and basically indicates whether the business is solvent on a short-term basis. If longer-term purchases are financed on overdraft the cur-rent liabilities side of the calculation increases and you potentially get a 'Net Current Deficit' making the business more vulnerable to financial shocks.

Although an overdraft should be temporary, an overdraft facility or 'limit' agreed by a bank can be an ongoing facility to cover regular shortfalls at cer-tain stages in the month or quarter. An example may be that certain bills have to be paid early in the month but regular income comes later in the month, with an overdraft facility being utilised to cover this regular shortfall.

In considering an overdraft facility or limit a bank will normally expect to see some kind of 'cashflow forecast'. This may be drawn up by an accountant but in simple cases you could use a simple spreadsheet to schedule expected income and expenditure shown on a weekly or daily basis, and identifying how much overdrawn the account may go and for how long. For the reasons mentioned above a cashflow forecast would normally show the account in credit at the end of the term as overdrafts should be temporary.

Overdraft facilities are normally agreed for up to a maximum of one year. A bank would normally expect a full review of the facility at least annually, with new cashflow forecasts and other financial accounts being produced.

Overdrafts that become permanent, i.e. the account does not swing back into credit on a regular basis, are sometimes referred to as having a 'hardcore'. The hardcore element is the amount of the minimum overdraft seen, i.e. the amount that never gets cleared at any time during the month. Hardcore overdrafts, particularly if the hardcore is increasing, can be the sign of financial problems as it indicates that the business is not generating enough cash to cover its regular costs. In such circumstances a review should take place to establish what has gone wrong. It may be that an expected temporary expense (perhaps a locum) has gone on longer than expected but will soon come to an end or it could be more serious, reflecting that losses are being made.

If the hardcore has resulted from an expected temporary overdraft occurring for longer than planned a bank may suggest any hardcore is transferred to a loan to help clear it and manage finances. However, be aware that this will only be effective provided the business reviews its operations and ensures the income to costs situation has improved.

One of the most common issues with an overdraft is when expenditure that should be on loan is paid for from an overdraft; an example is premises improvements. A few small items, a 'lick of paint', etc. may be acceptable being paid from the current account as a sundry cost, but larger items such as major refits or extensions should normally be financed via a loan. A simple rule is whether the cost can be covered from free cashflow in under a year.

Charges for overdraft facilities will vary but may include an 'Arrangement Fee', interest and possibly a monthly or monitoring fee. The arrangement fee will normally be a percentage of the amount required, e.g. 1.5% of the overdraft requested, payable up front and regardless of how much you actually use the facility. Interest rates are normally linked to base rate and as such will fluctuate with base rate. Interest however is only charged on the amount of the borrowing actually used, which means if you avoid an overdraft in one charging period you should not pay any interest.

RECRUITMENT – PARTNER, SALARIED GP OR LOCUM?

Mike Gilbert

Retirement or the expansion of services will necessitate a practice to recruit. If the practice has a choice, they need to plan accordingly and consider whether they require a partner, salaried GP, locum or indeed an alternative health professional. The problem medical practices face today is that they may have no choice as in many parts of the country recruitment has become a nightmare and practices are almost obliged to take anyone who is available irrespective of status.

Assuming the practice has a choice let us consider the merits or otherwise of each course of action.

The locum GP

According to a recent survey, a locum in England can cost on average £475 per day plus of course employers' superannuation contributions, which are now met by the practice. One is tempted to conclude that long-term locums are an expensive option and that short-term locums should be taken on only when there is an identifiable and justifiable need.

Larger practices of five or more partners should look to internal locums whenever possible and constantly review their rotas. The financial implications of internal locums could well 'even up' between the partners over the course of a year.

There are of course other problems associated with recruiting a locum GP. By definition a locum will work 'in' the practice and not 'on' the practice so that they will not be involved at all in management issues. They must learn or be trained to use the practice systems and protocols so that they do not damage the 'brand' in any way.

In the context of long-term recruitment locum GPs are probably a last resort, unless of course they express a desire for career enhancement in the practice, otherwise they are not a solution to any succession issues. The best form of locum is probably a retired partner who knows the 'ropes' and no longer pays pension contributions.

The salaried GP

According to a recent HSCIC report, a salaried GP earns an average £49,300 per annum working 5.4 sessions. This equates to £73,037 per annum for 8 sessions, which, together with the on-cost of employers' superannuation and employers' NIC, could amount to £90,000 per annum. This means that, if the salaried GP works 230 days a year, the daily rate becomes £391, which is less than the cost of a GP locum.

The introduction of salaried GPs was to create some flexibility within the profession, recognising in the main the common need to change location, but the jury is out with regard to the success or otherwise of this initiative. Given that a salaried GP is not an 'owner' of the practice, they also by definition work 'in' and not 'on' the practice. Indeed, if they take on a management role then they may as well be a partner.

In the employment contract it is essential to include a clause that enforces a salaried GP to adopt all of the systems and protocols of the practice in order to protect the brand. They may have the skills to assist the practice in providing additional services, and this should be encouraged.

In the context of long-term recruitment salaried GPs have a role to play, but the practice must ensure there are sufficient partners to undertake the necessary management roles. For practices on average or above earnings, salaried GPs are financially attractive, but for practices on low earnings they are also an expensive option.

Given the pace of change in medical practice, we are noticing instances where alternative healthcare professionals, such as pharmacists, are being recruited as an alternative to a salaried GP. The cost implications are similar, but the final decision will rest on the needs of the locality rather than finance. On the surface, a salaried GP (or other health professional) is a more viable option than a locum GP.

The GP partner

The over-riding driver in recruiting a partner is the issue of succession. So far as concerns cost, a partner on a profit share of £115,000 per annum (after paying employers' superannuation contributions) working 230 days a year creates a daily rate of £500, which is of course more than a salaried GP or locum but not that much.

Nonetheless great care needs to be exercised when recruiting a partner. Partnership is like a marriage and demands the same precautions. A new partner must have the same visions and philosophies as the continuing partners, and be able and committed to the management of the practice.

A partner must work 'on' as well as 'in' the practice and be given defined management roles. He or she must be prepared to go along with the majority and be committed to the agreed systems and protocols or brand of the practice. In other words a new partner must be an appropriate candidate for the post and not just another 'pair of hands'. It is pointless to recruit a partner who undertakes clinical sessions and then disappears to undertake a lucrative private post that is of no benefit to the practice. Rather, he or she should be an ambassador of the practice at all times and part of a team all moving in the same direction. All partners should aim to leave a great legacy to the partners of the future.

All in all difficult decisions have to be made, but the key to success is to find the right person who fits with the practice philosophy, and to run a practice in a way that it becomes an attractive environment for younger GPs. In the current climate this may be almost impossible to achieve but existing partners must use lateral thinking when advertising posts. Succession has to be dealt with at an early stage or you will end up with management by crisis, because the laws of supply and demand will prevail. Given the current tales of mounting workloads, falling incomes and burnout, how will we ever encourage medical students to pursue a career in medical practice? Would you want your child to become a GP?

RETIREMENT AND PENSIONS – WHAT DECISIONS SHOULD GPs MAKE?

Kevin Walker

For most GPs who qualified in the early 1980s the classic song 'Should I Stay or Should I Go' by the Clash in 1982 may be memorable. It is, however, a question I am often asked by GPs who are now in their mid-to-late 50s.

The continued pressure on the NHS and the additional pressure put on GPs and practice managers has become intolerable for many. This, coupled with the continued 'attack' on NHS pensions, has most GPs questioning whether it is worthwhile being a member of the NHS scheme.

In very simple terms for most GPs the answer is yes!

The combination of higher member payments and increased taxation due to the Annual Allowance (AA) and the Lifetime Allowance (LTA) has made people question their membership. The most common questions I get asked from GPs at the moment is: when can I afford to retire as I have now had enough, and how will the reduction in both the LTA and the AA affect me? Should I remain a member of the scheme or should I opt out of the scheme?

The decision to stay in, of course, is based upon an average life expectancy and state of health. It is all very well having a bigger pension in your late 70s or early 80s but if at that point in time you are dead or in a nursing home with a gold-plated walking frame then what is the point? Would it be far better coming out of the scheme early and enjoying the benefits with a far better quality of life now while you can enjoy the money?

From 2014/15 the AA, which is the increase of the value of a pension each year, has reduced to £40k from £50k. In addition, the total value of the pension scheme when you retire – the LTA – has been reduced from £1.5m to £1.25m. Now let us look at some of the impacts of the changes to the AA and the LTA.

Annual Allowance

This is the amount of money you are allowed to save in your pension each year before the government applies tax penalties. If you break the AA then you will be faced with a tax penalty. Let us say that you have used up £50k and the AA is £40k; you are £10k over the limit. If you breach the allowance then you can look at the previous three years and carry forward unused allowances.

If there is nothing to carry forward then £10k is treated as extra income and taxed at the doctor's marginal rate. In a worst-case example, if your taxable income that year was £100k then you will end up with a 60% tax charge on that £10k. This is because once your income exceeds £100k the government reduces your personal allowance so the effective tax rate on that slice would be 60%. Ouch! If the AA tax charge exceeds £2k then you can elect to get the pension scheme to pay.

If the scheme pays then the NHS uses an actuarial factor and it charges you interest at 3% plus CPI inflation until the benefits are taken, and even then the NHS can change this. It might be cheaper to use a payday lender!

POINTS TO CONSIDER
- Have you received an AA statement yet and do you have an AA problem?
- If you are paying Added Years, which is increasing your AA and LTA problems, should you stop them?
- If you had an AA tax charge for 2011/12 onwards then how do you know if you have paid the right tax and was the AA statement correct?
- For 2013/14 you will have until 31 July 2015 to decide if the scheme pays but you must have completed your tax return by 31 January 2015, indicating your choice.

As this is an extremely complex subject, professional independent advice from a regulated adviser should be sought before making any decisions.

Lifetime Allowance
The LTA is the amount of money you are allowed to have in your pension fund when you come to retire, before the government once again applies tax penalties.

If you breach the allowance when you come to retire then there is an effective 55% tax charge, but that is not the way the tax charge is actually applied in practice.

As previously mentioned, the LTA has been reduced to £1.25m with effect from April 2014, and if you are above that limit at that point in time then decisions will need to be made with regards to your options. If you opted for Fixed Protection 14 then you will have benefit accrual if you stayed in the scheme and you must notify HMRC or penalties will be applied by them.

If you have stayed in the scheme, this benefit accrual will mean that you will be tested against the reduced £1.25m limit. You should consider applying for Individual Protection 14 (IP14) and the value of your benefits accrued as at 5 April 2014 will be your personal limit. If you are between £1.25m and £1.5m then this is your limit. If you are above £1.5m then the maximum you can protect is £1.5m.

You will have up until 5 April 2017 to apply for IP14 and the NHS says it will issue valuations in 2016. Bearing in mind the problem with issuing accurate AA statements, would you trust that they are accurate?

If you do opt out of the scheme, then you are no longer an active member of the scheme with regards to the Death in Service benefits and your family would be worse off than had you died in service. This needs to be taken into consideration before deciding to opt out of the pension scheme.

There is, of course, no guarantee about how long you will live after you retire and in the future you should have no mortgage and hopefully no dependent children! This means the amount of money you require in your long-term retirement, depending on your standard of living, is substantially less than what you believe.

The question that therefore raises its head again is: can you prove that staying in the pension scheme is the right thing to do and do you want to be substantially better off in your late 70s and early 80s, which is only good if you are still fit and healthy at that point in time? Or would you rather have more money now to enjoy when you are fit and able, and have a better quality of life now than in your later retirement years? Is this just about the numbers or is it about quality of life?

Things to do

1   Obtain an updated, accurate NHS pension statement and have a qualified individual produce calculations to show what the relevant value of your LTA value will be as at 5 April 2014.
2   When does the GP intend to retire? If you applied for FP14 should that be changed to IP14?

Due to the complicated nature of the subject, you would be well advised not to take any action without discussing the implications of how the AA and the LTA will affect you personally with an independent adviser. There are a number of different options for you to consider when you are near or in excess of the LTA value.

1   Retire immediately and take your benefits.
2   Defer your benefits.
3   Take your benefits under the 24-hour retirement rules.

For many doctors who have exceeded their LTA value, who are in their mid-to-late 50s, the 24-hour retirement rule may be particularly attractive. By using the early retirement factors under the NHS pension scheme you can substantially reduce the LTA charge.

Of course, the pension taken will not be as great as the pension you would have received had you remained in service until the age of 60, even with the penalties. However, you would have had those additional pension payments in the meantime. You may have to live in the region of 20 years after you have retired to catch up for this lost income.

This again begs the question: would you rather be better off now when you are fit and healthy than being better off in your late 70s or early 80s?

This is where individual advice is required. It is simply a question of the best mathematical answer or the best quality of life answer and this must be provided by an independent qualified person who is regulated by the Financial Conduct Authority and can deliver objective advice.

So should I stay or should I go?

Now that is the question.

Kevin Walker,
NHS Pension Specialist,
BW Medical Accountants/Blackett Walker Ltd,
Independent Financial Adviser

Blackett Walker is authorised and regulated by the Financial Conduct Authority.

GOING FOR GOLD

Mike Gilbert

In difficult times, maximising profits in the NHS and protecting GP earnings into the future are crucial issues facing medical practice. However, in order to deal with the future we need to know where we are starting from. For the sake of argument only, let us assume that the average earnings of a full-time equivalent GP are £117,000 per annum. Obviously, this figure can vary upwards or downwards depending upon whether the practice operates under a Personal Medical Services (PMS) or General Medical Services (GMS) contract, or whether the practice has the ability to dispense. This figure is higher than that quoted by the Health and Social Care Information Centre because the latter takes an average of all GPs based on their tax returns, which does not recognise full-time equivalent status.

Although this average provides us with a starting measure, it conceals the real issue with regard to GP earnings, which is not the average but the extremely wide range of earnings. In the experience of Association of Independent Specialist Medical Accountants (AISMA) members, it is not uncommon to visit two very similar practices in one day where in the first practice the average earnings of a full-time equivalent GP are, say, £160,000 p.a. and in the second practice they are £70,000 p.a. So what is the difference? It seems to have very little to do with geography, deprivation, patient demand or rurality, but everything to do with the MENTALITY of the partners in the practice.

By compiling the annual survey into the earnings of full-time equivalent GPs, which includes a third of all GPs in the UK, AISMA members have been able to identify certain features of the higher and lower earners. This has led them to conclude on what it takes to maximise profits.

Here are some of the findings:

Features of low earners
- Practices involved in partnership disputes.
- Practices with inadequate resources, such as staff, equipment and space.
- Badly organised practices with poor internal controls and usually an excessive number of patients.
- GPs who are bad managers of time.

- GPs who work as individuals and not as a team, who gave little or no thought to fundholding, early entry into PMS or involvement in commissioning.
- New practices with low list sizes.
- Practices in very deprived areas.
- GPs who value time off over and above money, and who incur very high deputising costs.
- GPs with poor patient data, either through neglect or poor skills mix amongst the staff.

Features of high earners
- Stable partnership (low turnover of partners).
- Partners work as a team and trust each other, plan ahead and meet regularly.
- Partners have similar philosophies in terms of the dichotomy between patient care, lifestyle and money.
- Proactive rather than reactive teams.
- Good managers of time.
- Well-organised GPs with strong staff teams and good skills mix amongst them.
- GPs who delegate well to nurses, health visitors, etc.
- GPs who work long hours, have low deputising costs and a high level of non-NHS earnings.
- Single-handed practitioners with very high list sizes (or indeed partnerships with more than average patient lists).
- GPs who have the ability to dispense or rent space to pharmacists.
- GPs who have taken advantage of PMS growth funding to free up time to perform more lucrative work.
- GPs who are heavily involved with their Clinical Commissioning Group (CCG).
- GPs with the most competent and skilled practice managers and specialist accountants.
- GPs who were early fundholders and have an involvement in commissioning or providing services.
- Practices with top-rate databases on patients and treatments.

Practices can mark themselves against the above criteria. A mark of 120 or more is good, a mark of 90 or more is average, and a mark of less than 90 is poor, where 10 marks are allocated for each bullet point.

Armed with all of the above we have been able to conclude on the key to financial success. It is all about recognising that you are running a business and managing 'TIME'. In this context it is imperative to distinguish between what is important and what is urgent, undertake the important tasks and delegate the urgent tasks wherever possible. The high earners work 'on' as well as 'in' the practice, and this can often be achieved by holding 'away days' to formulate the business strategy of the practice. Conversely, the low earners tend to commit financial suicide by doing nothing 'on' the practice and expecting a different outcome. What becomes clear is that the proper management of time creates at first greater enjoyment, which is then followed by greater earnings. The following may help in time management:

- create an organisation chart, with clear lines of responsibility
- have proper and appropriate partner roles
- constantly review and modify all systems
- review job specifications and training needs
- manage patient demand
- hold 'all hands' meetings on a quarterly basis
- hold monthly formal partner meetings that are properly minuted and acted upon
- write and buy into a procedures manual.

The above conclusion confirms the phrase 'reality is what you perceive clearly'. Research into the high and low earners of the medical profession has created this perception, which is indeed a reality. Only by the management of time can practices take steps to maintain or improve profitability. Once achieved, some of the key issues to consider may be as follows:

- quality points
- bidding for single-handed or primary care organisation (PCO)-run practices (remember to look for contractual income of about £140 per patient)
- calculate your costs as a percentage of total income, which should be a maximum of 60%
- consider dispensing, which might be an opportunity for practices alone or by way of joint venture
- look at level of outside income (the average per full-time equivalent GP is £22,500)
- review level of enhanced services and consider whether you need to specialise to become providers or indeed federate with other practices
- watch your list size as money follows the patient.

Having reviewed the above key issues, the next stage is to recognise potential quick-win situations, which can broadly be summarised as follows:

- bidding for practices currently run by a PCO
- merger or takeover of smaller practices
- getting involved in provisioning even if this involves specialising, in such areas as:
  - cardiology
  - the elderly

- diabetes
- palliative medicine
- mental health
- substance misuse
- dermatology
- musculoskeletal conditions
- women and children
- ENT
- homeless/asylum seekers
- procedures, e.g. vasectomy or endoscopy
- sports medicine
- getting involved with your CCG so that you are aware of the needs of the locality and provide the service accordingly. This may be more lucrative than private work
- delegating routine tasks to nurses, pharmacists and other health professionals
- agreeing with your partners where you stand regarding patient care, quality of life and money
- carefully pursuing lucrative outside appointments (see Appendix).

It cannot be denied that time management creates the opportunity to pursue lucrative outside appointments, but practices must always calculate the opportunity cost. This means that you always have to measure the benefit of the outside appointment against the cost of what you are giving up – there is always a trade-off. Beware of the pitfalls of this approach, such as:

- ego trip – flattery, title or status are nice but is a GP a better person for simply filling a vacant post?
- escapism – getting away from the surgery may be great but what is the opportunity cost?
- partner resentment – can resentment occur if income is not pooled?
- delegation in return – you cannot compress existing surgery work into a shorter time unless you delegate properly. Determine how busy you should be. Letting work mount up is not the way to maximise profit.

As further consideration in the pursuit of maximising profits, consider how to contain costs. This might be achieved by the following:

- delegating to practice managers, but do not abdicate as there have been too many horror stories
- joining buying consortiums, e.g. for the purchase of medical supplies
- using internal rather than external locums
- shopping about for special deals, but remember you get what you pay for when it comes to specialist advice.

At the end of the day GPs must realise that medical practice is now a business. The highest earners will be those practices that have the:

- right structures
- right roles
- right services
- right technology
- right people
- right premises.

The future is certainly going to be a challenge!

AWAY DAY – PLANNING FOR THE FUTURE

Mike Gilbert

When formulating the future strategy of the practice, many GPs often find it difficult to get started. Perhaps the best approach is to hold an 'away day', possibly facilitated by a consultant or a specialist practice accountant. The object of the 'away day' is to produce a plan, probably in written form, albeit brief and to the point. To achieve this, practices need an agenda and set out below is a guide that may help the process.

There are a number of prerequisites for any away day, which can broadly be summarised as follows:

- involve the practice manager either as a facilitator or an integral part of the team
- record all major points by means of a number of flipcharts
- all partners must contribute on an equal basis, but be totally honest throughout without being hurtful or unnecessarily aggressive
- no anecdotes – phrases such as 'in my day' or 'we always used to …' are banned
- no zingers – niggling at each other will not help at all
- have plenty of refreshments (but preferably not alcoholic).

The agenda for an away day should centre around six key questions as follows:

Six key questions	Information to consider
1 What do we want to do?	The personal aspirations of the partners regarding health care, earnings, general goals and environment.
2 What have we done in the past?	A critical analysis of current and past performance.
3 What must we do well to succeed?	The key success factors.
4 What could we do?	The strengths and weaknesses in terms of resources: skills, staffing, space, finance, etc.
5 What might we do?	The opportunities and threats in a changing environment.
6 What should we do?	The identification and evaluation of a range of options arising from questions (1) to (5).

The above merely *states* the 'bare bones' of the discussion and there may be considerable overlap. To provide more 'flesh on the bone' we set out below the sorts of issues that are likely to be considered under each of the key questions.

Question 1: what do we want to do?
- The balance between money and the quality of life.
- How much do you want to earn? How many hours per week do you want to work?
- Organisation chart and lines of authority.
- Partner roles.
- Partnership succession.
- Outside appointments versus NHS.
- Desires to specialise.

Question 2: what have we done in the past?
- How well is the business organised?
- What hours do we currently spend on professional activities?
- How does our earning compare with national averages?
- How good are we compared with others?

Question 3: what must we do well to succeed?
- The key success factors are normally the essential 'drivers'.
- State-of-the-art premises and information technology systems.
- Structuring the practice properly.
- Delegation of routine tasks.
- Everybody in their correct role?
- Providing the correct services to meet the needs of patients.

Question 4: what could we do?
- What are our strengths and weaknesses?
- Do the partners have the necessary skills?
- Have we got the right staff?
- Are our premises suitable to face the future provision of primary care?
- Do we have the appropriate clinical support in our staffing?
- Are our finances well organised?
- Do we have a good reputation?
- Do we deal appropriately with training needs?
- Do we get on well as a team, meet regularly, and work on the practice as well as in the practice?
- Do we provide the right services?
- Do we have appropriate prescribing and referral patterns?
- Are we happy with our practice profile, quality of health care and list size?

Honesty in considering the practice strengths and weaknesses is crucial.

Whereas question 4 is rather inward looking, question 5 considers what is happening outside the practice.

Question 5: what might we do?

- What is currently happening to our profession in terms of NHS direction, government intervention and the provision of health care generally?
- Who are our competition and what threats do they pose?
- Might we recruit other healthcare professionals to provide new or improved services?
- Should we train to obtain a specialisation (such as dermatology) that we can 'sell' to the CCG in the form of enhanced services, or by way of provisioning?
- Can we delegate better to free up our time to take on lucrative outside appointments?
- Might we find land to build a health centre providing a full range of services as owners with selected tenants?
- Are we properly embracing practice-based commissioning and provisioning?
- Have we the resources to 'bid' for other practices?
- Does dispensing provide an opportunity?
- Are there opportunities to obtain income from outside activities?
- Can we achieve more quality points?
- Are there opportunities to reduce costs?

Question 6: what should we do?

Having spent most of the day on questions 1 to 5, it is now time to summarise the practice objectives and philosophy, and list all the issues the practice is going to address. It is now decision time and all agreed decisions should be written down in the form of a plan. Every decision must state who is responsible for carrying out the task and in what timescale. There should be follow-up meetings to discuss progress, perhaps on a quarterly basis.

To achieve the greatest benefit from an away day, GPs must accept from the outset that a medical practice is a business and success will not be achieved without the:

- right structures
- right roles
- right services
- right technology
- right people
- right premises.

PRIVATE WORK AVAILABLE

Mike Gilbert

Here is a '100 ways of obtaining private income' checklist. The list, of course, is not exhaustive but at least provides a guide as to what might be available:

- acupuncture sessions
- authorship fees
- bail hostel fees
- benefits agency work
- biopsy clinics
- blue badge examinations
- Clinical Commissioning Group (CCG) board fees
- CCG compensatory allowance
- CCG meeting fees
- character references
- committee fees – British Medical Association (BMA)
- committee fees – General Medical Council (GMC)
- committee fees – medical defence union
- committee fees – Royal College of General Practitioners (RCGP)
- coroners' court reports and attendance
- court of protection reports and certificates
- court reports and attendance fees
- cremation fees
- data collection
- deputising income – agencies
- deputising income – cooperatives
- deputising income – rotas
- directorships – ambulance trusts
- directorships – cooperatives
- directorships – deputising
- drug company – research
- drug company – trials
- hire of rooms – NHS
- hire of rooms – other health professionals
- hospice appointments
- hospital work – NHS bed fund
- hospital work – NHS casualty service

- hospital work – NHS clinical assistant
- hospital work – NHS practitioner
- hospital work – private
- hypnotherapy sessions
- impotency clinics
- independent tribunal service
- lecturing fees
- life assurance reports
- local initiatives – diabetes, smoking, ischaemic heart disease, etc.
- Local Medical Committee (LMC) chair/secretary
- locum work
- Macmillan service
- medical audit advisory group work
- medicals – government departments
- medicals – health authority
- medicals – local authority
- medico-legal work
- mentoring fees
- minor surgery – excess over General Medical Services (GMS)
- minor surgery – non-GMS
- minor surgery – vasectomies
- monitoring – anticoagulant, methadone, etc.
- NHS Direct fees
- NHS Direct posts
- NHS trust board fees
- NSPCC
- occupational health
- passport counter-signature
- pharmacy joint ventures
- pilot licence reports and examinations
- police surgeon
- police training centre retainer
- private consultancy work
- private medical examinations and reports
- private prescriptions
- private vaccinations – yellow fever, travel, etc.
- public health appointments
- reports – Department of Health, Social Services and Public Safety
- reports – insurance companies
- reports – solicitors
- retainer – air force
- retainer – airports
- retainer – army
- retainer – commercial
- retainer – industrial

- retainer – local authority
- retainer – media
- retainer – nursing homes
- retainer – police
- retainer – prison
- retainer – retail
- retainer – residential homes
- retainer – school
- retainer – university
- retainer – young offenders
- review panel – disciplinary
- shotgun licence certificates
- sick notes
- sports – club doctor for various sports
- sports – event attendance
- sports – injury clinics
- sports – rugby football club doctor
- summative assessments
- teaching fees – medical school
- undergraduate training
- visiting medical officer – local authority
- vocational training course organiser
- war pension domestic visits

INDEX

Lightning Source UK Ltd.
Milton Keynes UK
UKOW04f1821131016

285243UK00002B/6/P